snakes

Also by Patricia Damery
Farming Soul: A Tale of Initiation
ISBN 978-1-926715-01-8

snakes

a novel

patricia damery

il piccolo editions
by

This is a work of fiction. Names, characters, places, and incidents either are the product of the author's imagination or are used fictitiously, and any resemblance to actual persons, living or dead, business establishments, events or locales is entirely coincidental.

Snakes

Fisher King Press
PO Box 222321
Carmel, CA 93922
www.fisherkingpress.com
+1-831-238-7799

For those who stayed
and those who left.

Lying Fallow

ONE

Though paleontological details are lacking, there is a great deal of information regarding the long association of snakes and man and his activities. The record is a composite of fact and fancy, with the latter still accepted as truth by many people.

—Will Barker, *Familiar Snakes and Amphibians of America*

1

"I can't imagine leaving a door open without a screen," she said. "Anything could come in. Anything!" You and I both know what she meant.

I see it smooth its way through the door, tongue darting in and out. Where would a snake go? Would it coil between the refrigerator and wall where I stuff the paper sacks? Would it find the cabinet door under the sink ajar and crawl into the empty space behind the garbage? …Or would it find its way to my bed? I picture myself pushing my bare feet and legs against fresh sheets, slipping toward sleep, when I brush a cool body with my foot. I raise the sheet to see it patterned there. I hear myself screaming, hysterically calling for the men to come out of the fields. Come, there is a snake in my bed, in the basement, in the yard. Come get the snake.

But we were 2500 miles away from those fields, and my mother was helping me prepare the evening meal. First trip after all these years, and she was already criticizing my home and habits! We were awkward without you. It felt like you must be just out of view, in the living room dozing or outside for a walk. I had to stop myself from calling, "Dad, do you want some iced tea?" I still could not believe you were dead.

"Do you want me to peel some potatoes?" she asked.

"No, Mama, I leave the skins on. But you could chop up some onions."

She clicked her tongue in disapproval. The air was humid with discomfort, and I retreated into memory. Mama, Dorothy, and I are in the basement next to the wringer washing machine. Mama reaches for the Clorox and grabs a snake instead. For a moment she can't let go, like she's grabbed an electric fence. Then she shrieks. The next thing I remember, we are driving to the field to get you. The car door slams behind Mama, and she walks down the rows to meet you. Her dress flaps about her knees as she waits in an ocean of glistening, green soybeans. Your eyes are expectant and worried as you brake the tractor and climb down to talk to her. Then your face rests into acceptance. Dorothy and I wave to you as you follow us home in your pickup.

I never watched you kill a snake, and now I will never know how you did it. This particular day you disappear into the basement with a hoe and return with the dead snake dangling from the end. You carry it to the road. You always said the road is the place the snake truly dies and that snakes do not die until sundown. To leave one in the grass or to toss it in a ditch or field is to release it. Soon it will be back in the yard or basement. I believe it becomes one with the shiny asphalt night road, connecting that neat, tidy farmland to the dark beyond.

Are you in the dark beyond? I wonder if you slipped from that suit you wore 750 Sundays, the one they cut down the back so they could dress you and lay you on the pink satin. Did you leave us to our mourning, kiss the earth, and go the way of the snake?

Mama finished the onions and we sat at the table on the deck outside the kitchen door.

"Do you remember the time I was playing with Tim Willard?" I asked. "The time he chased me with the two-foot rubber snake?" My mind's eye searched for the details of that day: Mama has gone to Peoria; Dorothy and I stay at Willard's until you are done in the field. Tim loves to tease us, and while Dorothy is napping, he produces a lifelike rubber snake and chases me around the yard. I scream in utter abandon and terror. We circle the house three times before you turn into the driveway to pick me up.

Here in my kitchen, these many years later, Mama liked the tale. But her smile was fragile, like winter sun.

I continued. "Remember how Grandma Moffet and Grandma Galway were in the front seat beside Dad?" The story unfolded in my mind, and I feel it as if for the first time. I run to the truck in relief. My dad is here! Come get the snake. Dad... You open the door, ready to grab Tim. I crawl over you but, by then, my grandmothers are also screaming and crawling over each other to get away from the open door. So we all scream. Grandma Galway's voice is hoarse and un-practiced, like a foghorn. Grandma Moffet's scream trickles up and down, over and over. My strong, even shrill is their backup. We are a trio of helplessness becoming rage becoming helplessness, vibrating with an intensity we almost never experience in the quiet duty of the rest of our lives. For a few moments pure emotion rules. Then, while you lead Tim Willard to his mother, we collapse, released from the hold of the snake.

Mama laughed as if she'd never heard the story. By the time Kristen woke, we were both relaxed and at home with each other. In our family snake stories do this, reminding us of our common fears and how we have always dealt with them, despite all odds.

Kristen squalled. "I'll bet she's hungry," I said, starting to get up. My breasts tingled with milk.

"Let me get her for you, Angela," Mama said, disappearing into the hallway.

2

I regret that you will never know Kristen. I've enjoyed her more than anything in my life. Of course, I love Trent and Wheat. But I have always worried with them and I still do. Each step of the way is new territory. When they were infants I agonized over every fever, when to introduce solid foods, how to prepare toddler Trent for the birth of his brother. When Trent entered kindergarten I felt as if he had died, I was so grief stricken. I agonized over Wheat's loneliness until he, too, entered kindergarten. Now, as they near adolescence, neither want to go most places with me or our family. I knew this time was coming. I tried to prepare myself for it. But when I saw Trent's lips curled back on his strong, white teeth, saying, "No, I don't want to go shopping, especially with you!" it came sooner than I anticipated. Wheat, of course, proclaimed his own independence immediately thereafter, and now, at ages 12 and 11, they won't be seen with me in shopping malls.

But Kristen. Kristen is happiest these days being an appendage. I am her world. At three months she is plump and smiles, kicking both her arms and legs as she watches me. At night she lies by my side, nursing. I awaken five hours later and she still slumbers. The slightest movement sets her mouth into motion, and if I lie very quietly, after five sucks, her mouth stops.

Sometimes Jake will curl against my back and cup her head in his hand. Her hair is like satin ribbons. Sometimes he says, "Angela, Kristen will get used to this."

"She's only three months," I say. "This won't last forever." But I let him put her in her own bed the next night until her first feeding. Then she spends the rest of the night attached to me.

I have lost little sleep with Kristen. I dream of dolphins, swimming, playing, as she lies beside me. With Trent and then Wheat, I sat in a chair at midnight, and then 2:00 a.m. and 6:00 a.m. I savored the calmness that came with sleepiness. My ears strained for the gulping noises, the short sniffs, and later, as they lay on my shoulder, their deep, noisy breaths. The yeasty mustard diapers assured me that all was well. I was swallowed and assimilated and reborn to feed.

But with Kristen I swim. She is my baby dolphin; we smooth the salty waters together. We make each turn attuned to the other's smell, the other's breathing and movement. I study the puffed lips between her legs as I change her diapers, pleased to have birthed another like me.

Mama promised to visit after you died last June, and now she's here for three weeks. I've never missed you more. When I met the plane, Mama and I hugged, tears obscuring the masses of travelers moving past us. I could feel your absence. You never visited. I know you were busy and cash was tight. But I've daydreamed about how it might have been had you come just once. You'll never see our house here high above the Russian River. You'll never sit on the sunny eastern deck and smell the pungent California bay laurel. You'll never know the tawniness of California summer meadows.

Driving home from the airport, we passed through rolling pasturelands. Mama took one look at the browned hills rolling upon themselves and said, "Is there a drought?"

"No, Mama, it doesn't rain during the summer."

"At home," she said, "if the land looked like this in June, we'd get federal funding for disaster relief."

As we drove through San Francisco, she was startled by the closeness of the buildings. "Do they have windows on the walls in between?" she asked. We crossed the Golden Gate Bridge in rush hour traffic at a slow crawl. "How can you drive in this traffic!" Perhaps she felt a threat in the sailboats whipped by the wind across the bay like tumbleweed across wintering fields. And here, in the redwoods, maybe she fears the forest has grown about me like a witch's circle and that I am lost to her.

3

I heard my mother cooing to Kristen long before she reappeared in the hallway. Her feet were heavy on the stairs. "Come on, sweetie, your mommy is waiting upstairs," she said. Kristen was quiet except for a few exuberant grunts. I rested my head on the back of the rocker, feeling more tired than I realized. My eyes fell automatically on the large expanse of white on the far wall near the ceiling. "You mean you are going to take the giant vulva weaving down?" Jake teased yesterday before I went to the airport. "It's not a vulva," I said lowly so Trent and Wheat would not hear. "So why are you taking it down?"

She might have liked the weaving. Besides, removing it left quite a gaping, blank space. Not that there aren't other weavings. I have weavings on almost every available surface. Marcy Wheeler, my closest friend who taught me to weave, told me once our home reminded her of a tent.

Kristen was stretching to find me when Mama reached the end of the hall. When Kristen saw me she lunged forward.

"Hold it, sweetheart." Mama laughed. "This baby is hungry!"

Kristen dropped into the crook of my arm and panted until I let her nurse. Then she gulped loudly. Mama settled onto the couch beside me. Kristen looks so much like her, with her wavy, chestnut hair, large, brown eyes, and moon-shaped face. So unlike you and me and the fair-haired Galways.

Mama studied the walls. "So how's your weaving?" she asked after a time.

How is my weaving? "Fine." What can be said? It is a quiet occupation. Kristen will sit in her baby seat beside me, but no one else can tolerate the boredom. Wheat used to watch, sunk in a beanbag chair, until he dropped off for a nap, but he doesn't take naps anymore.

It's like plowing, I wanted to say. You go over and over and over again. Each movement, as insignificant as it may seem, is essential. The slightest inattention or neglect will show in the end. The rest will lie neat and woven, but there will be that flaw, and that is what will be remarkable.

"Are you selling much?" Mama pressed, eyeing the blank spot on the far wall.

"No." I haven't tried. When the walls were covered, I folded my weavings and tucked them into closets in the children's rooms and hallway, and when the closets were full, in the drawers of the bureau in the living room. Now I'm filling a trunk in my studio. Sometimes I send a piece to someone for Christmas, but mostly, I cannot bear to part with them.

"I don't really want to sell my weavings."

"Well, I don't know why not. They are beautiful. You would have a good market for them."

Kristen was playing more than eating, so I placed her on my shoulder. She reached for her grandmother with a fat hand.

"Let me have this little rascal," Mama cooed. I let her hold Kristen while I got a clean diaper from the closet. Then I scooped Kristen into my hands and laid her on the floor. She giggled wildly.

Again, I found myself wishing you were here. You would probably have been sitting in Jake's chair over by the woodstove, and you would have said something like, "Angela, I remember when you were that size. You had the bluest eyes!" After I finished nursing her, you would have played with Kristen as she lay on your lap, as you did with both the boys. Maybe she'd fall asleep there. Grandfathers have time to feel the eternity of an infant. There's just the baby and the time she demands of you. The hours open upon themselves, giving each tender baby touch an added numinosity. I know you didn't have time for this with me or Jimmy or Dorothy, though Trent and Wheat were graced with it. But now you won't with Kristen either.

My movements were quick, adept. I never used paper diapers with Trent and Wheat. It took some retraining to get used to a garbage pail full of white paper balls. I am, after all, an environmentalist. But the ease won out.

"Paper diapers make things so much easier," my mother commented. "I used to spend an hour a week hanging diapers out on the line."

I can still see her. I would sit in the grass by the clothes basket as she pinned Dorothy's diapers corner to corner on ropes webbing our backyard. She would snap each diaper in the wind, flip out its wrinkles, like worries, and leave it limp and relaxed to dance in the breezes. I ran beneath the damp diapers, letting them brush my face, and smelled the sun drying into them. Later I imagined the sun flak-

ing into tiny pieces to powder Dorothy's bottom. My paper replicas
with the built-in tabs and elastic leg bands are sadly lacking in sunlight.

"They are easier," I said, "but I miss the smell of line-dried diapers."

"You always were a romantic." There was a tone of sadness in her
voice and then the strained silence again. She cleared her throat in
the way I knew another story was coming. "I haven't told you about
Jimmy." She folded her hands on her lap. "He was driving on the
blacktop last week when he came upon what looked like a giant snake
stretched the entire width of the road. Old Wendell was just driving
up from the other direction. You can imagine where he'd been! Jimmy
said it's a wonder he could still drive the car. Anyway, they both got
out, and sure enough, it was a huge boa constrictor! Jimmy says Wendell was sure he'd been drinking too much when he saw that snake."
She laughed.

"I wonder where it came from," I said.

"I don't know, but Jimmy thinks it must have been somebody's
pet."

"What did he do?"

"He watched it crawl into the ditch, and then he drove on. He's
sure not going to bother a snake that size!"

"I wonder what happened to it," I said.

"I don't know," she said, "but around home a snake like that can't
survive very long. And it certainly couldn't make it through a winter."

4

You never knew Marcy Wheeler. I told her snake stories too, while
she taught me to weave. She lived in the Victorian next door to me
when I first moved to California. Everything about her seemed exotic

and yet also strangely familiar. She served honey-sweetened chamomile tea in small, handleless cups my first visit. Her house was full of looms and yarn. A large floor loom monopolized her sunporch. The piece she was working on had large clumps of thick yarn intermingled with shells and driftwood. In a corner of the sunporch stood a spinning wheel, and baskets with skeins of wool and llama yarns, Angora and mohair, sat on the floor everywhere. Marcy later showed me how to dye these fibers a warm terra-cotta with onionskins or a faint yellow with goldenrod. I came to love all the processes of weaving: collecting, carding, and spinning the yarns; collecting plants and dyeing the skeins; and, eventually, threading the loom and weaving the cloth. I loved the feel of the yarns on my fingers, the slow back-and-forth movement of the loom. It reminded me of the monotony of fieldwork and home.

Marcy belonged to a weavers' guild that used only hand-spun and home-dyed yarns. When she bought a new bunch of wool from a rancher on the coast, I recognized the pungent, penetrating smell of sheep the minute I walked in her door. That smell took me back to barns with manure ankle-deep, hot urine steaming on a bitter-cold night, sheep huddled together in a far corner, waiting for lambing and for the return of springtime grass. When I smelled my hands after spinning Marcy's wool, they smelled of lanolin. "Sheep taste the way they smell," you used to say. We didn't eat lamb; none of the farmers did, even after the Farm Bureau's attempt to change us over with free lamb barbecues.

Marcy collected this wool and sometimes wove it unwashed into a weave that was oily and watertight. Usually, though, she washed it so it more resembled the skeins that I was used to handling. At first, I just watched as Marcy used her thick, loosely wrapped skeins to weave her paradoxes. I watched her thread the flat wooden needle with red yarn to weave a sun "as hot as sin. I want it to be the source, primal and oozing, here, in this part of the piece." Her delicate fingers fanned over the still-to-be-woven warp threads. "And here," she said, pointing to the woven browns, greens, "here is the coolness, the place of solidness and nurturing and fecundity. I want the reds to bleed into the weaving, to permeate it and become its life pulse, so it is not so contained, neither the sun nor the earth." She showed me a sampler of how she planned to achieve this effect. She wanted the warp threads to show "so it will be as one."

After several weeks she convinced me to buy a used portable loom. I learned to thread the loom, to choose the weft and warp threads, to encourage a yarn into a weave with just the right tautness. I watched the result of my every movement grow into a larger and larger fabric. Marcy showed me how yarns and threads worked together, how colors merged when crossed, how to think of the whole piece when working on any one part. "The larger picture is in your heart," Marcy told me. "You must be completely here, where you are in the present place of your work, but in your heart you must know the whole, even if you can't see it in your mind. It is a feeling the work has."

Much of the time that we were weaving, we were silent, but if I asked Marcy a question, she immediately answered. She was not away; she did not have to travel back from some distant landscape.

"What about this weave?" I might ask. "I want it thicker through here but unvarying throughout the rest."

"Try this yarn," or, "Experiment. Trust your inclination and see what happens." And I would, with Marcy commenting, "I like the looser quality you've left here. It adds texture that contrasts with the tighter weave above it," or, "That color is abrupt but try it awhile and see what happens." Then we were silent again, the soft pushing of wooden needles and beaters competing only with a mockingbird outside or the buzzing of a fly against the glass of the sunporch window. There was a ripeness to the silence, a fleshiness, like a fig opened.

During those 10 months Marcy and I wove together, I told her our snake stories. I couldn't help it. When we stopped for tea, the stories spilled out of me. She was fascinated and her interest honed my own. What were these stories about anyway? Never had I considered that, as I also never considered what I had done in leaving you and the farm. Did you ever forgive me, Dad? You must have known that there wasn't room for me there. There wasn't room for my whole generation. But then again we both know that is not the whole story.

5

On the Sunday after Mama arrived, we were sitting on the deck outside the kitchen, eating a late breakfast when I heard Nester's muffled "Reow! "Reow!" I hate it when he drops the mutilated offerings of gophers and mice, baby birds and lizards at the door. Each morning entrails lie entangled in the webbing of the doormat, which I shake into the hedge on my way to get the paper. So assuming he had his usual, I was only disgusted until I saw a ruler-length, black snake dangling from his mouth. Screaming, I jumped up, bumping the table. My chair fell backward. Mama took one look and also screamed. Nester, of course, ran. Kristen began to cry. I reached for her but Jake, sitting next to her, picked her up first.

"Jesus Christ, Angela!" he said.

"Nester has a snake!" I screamed again.

Wheat was up by now. "I hope he hasn't killed him," he said. "Here, Nester! Oh, Mom, you scared him into the woodpile!"

"Don't let him drop that snake in the wood!" I cried.

"Would you calm down?" asked Jake. "You are scaring Kristen. You've spilled the tea. Would you just sit down?"

"Oh, Mr. Cool," I said. "Not everybody grew up with snakes in their playpen! I happen to be goddamn scared of them!"

"Angela!" Mama said. "The children..."

"The children, right!" chimed in Jake. "You're going to make Kristen scared of snakes if you keep acting like this."

"I hope I do! She'd be better off." I took Kristen from him and gently rubbed her back. She quieted. Mama went into the house and closed the door.

"Did you get him?" Trent asked nonchalantly.

"Nah, he ran off," Wheat answered. "I think the snake is dead anyway. It wasn't wiggling. Nester probably ate its head off."

Kristen stopped crying. I glared at Jake and he gave me a disgusted look.

"I can't help it," I said.

"You can try."

"Why? I hate them. I've always been this way."

"You can try, Angela. This is ridiculous. I can't believe we've got two kids who don't act as scared as you."

"So they survived me!"

Jake took this as a cue to make up and put an arm around me. "Yes, they survived you," he said. Kristen batted at his nose and giggled.

"Hey, Grandma, the snake is gone," yelled Wheat. "They won't hurt you anyway."

"Grandma knows that," said Trent.

"Then why does she scream?" asked Wheat.

"Same reason Mom does," answered Trent. Jake glanced at me.

Mama returned just as Wheat and Trent climbed the steps to the street. "We'll see if we can find Nester," Wheat called.

Mama looked at me sternly. "You really have to watch your language if you don't want your kids swearing."

"Who says I do?!" I exploded. "There are times and places for swearing, and one time is when there's a fucking snake on my deck and a husband bitching because I scream!"

"Angela!" She didn't know what else to say.

I looked at Jake. He rolled his eyes. "Okay," I said. "Okay, let's stop this conversation. It's getting nowhere." Mama looked relieved.

Trent and Wheat ran back down the steps. "He's gone," said Wheat.

"Yeah, well, where else would he be with all that yelling?" asked Trent. They are my husband's sons.

It was at this moment, just as things were quieting down and beginning to right themselves, that Wheat got the idea of introducing his pet snake to his grandmother. "Grandma, would you like to meet Vera?" he asked in his earnest 11-year-old voice.

"You haven't caught Vera, I hope," I asked anxiously.

Mama looked confused. "Caught her?" she asked.

"She's a snake!" blurted out Trent.

"But a good snake," Wheat added. "She'd be a good snake for you to meet."

Mama sat motionless and stunned.

"Grandma doesn't want to meet any snakes," I said, "not even good snakes."

Jake shook his head. "I can't believe this hysteria."

"Don't start in again," I said.

6

Jake and I have a long and sordid history with snakes. Take the one and only time I visited Jake's parents. They live in Williamsburg, a small college town in east Texas. Jake told me his father taught in the zoology department there, that he had three brothers, all younger, and that there was a bayou a block from his home where he and his brothers fished as he was growing up. He did not tell me that his father was a herpetologist, that he specialized in rare breeds of South American snakes, and that his house was a museum that could rival any reptile petting zoo in the country. He did not tell me, he said, because he wanted me to see the home where he grew up and to meet his parents there. It was his first deception, and one to which I should have paid more attention.

He did not plan on my meeting any of the snakes. That was an accident. He convinced his father to move the aquariums and tanks into the storage room in the back of the house for the week we would be staying. He also persuaded his father not to let the boas and pythons roam loose during our stay.

The visit began normally. We flew to Houston and spent the day there before driving north to Williamsburg. It was late afternoon before we reached the tree-lined street where Jake grew up. Jake pointed out the neighborhood grocery store where he used to buy penny candy and the alley that was a shortcut to the bayou. I sat next to him in the middle of the front seat. The vinyl stuck to the backs of my damp legs.

It was Easter vacation and there was a heat wave. Never had I been so hot at Easter. The open car windows allowed some breeze to circulate when we drove fast, but as we slowed for Jake's old street, the air hung in damp clumps. Thick, green leaves spanned the sky overhead as children ran barelegged and barefooted from yard to yard. When we pulled up in front of the monstrous white house with the large porch entry, I could see a woman at the open screen door. "Jake!" she called. The door slammed and she ran down the steps to meet us. Just as quickly, Jake hopped out of the car to meet her. "Why, Jake, you are still growing!" she said as she gave him a hug. "You look so good! … And this must be Angela!"

I had crawled out of the front seat and was standing a few feet from them. Jake introduced us, his voice reverberating to the soft lilt of his mother's Southern drawl.

"Call me Irene," she said as she extended a hand and then took my right arm and Jake's left and walked us into the house.

The house was a large five-bedroom home that the original owner bought out of a Sears catalog and had delivered, piece by numbered piece, to the lot. It felt cool inside, although it wasn't air-conditioned. A large wooden staircase curled upstairs at the front entry.

"Jake, why don't you get your suitcases, and I'll take Angela and get some iced tea."

So Jake went back to the car, and I followed Irene into the kitchen. A door opened onto a screened porch on the back wall. As Irene cracked cubes loose in the ice tray, I stole glances at the cupboards to my left and the dining area directly in front of me. I sat perched on a wooden stool that overlooked the cooking area. I couldn't think of a thing to say.

Irene was an attractive, youthful-looking woman. Her madras wraparound skirt just grazed her knees. "Do you like sugar in your tea, hon?"

"No thanks."

Jake reappeared. "I see you got Johnny's room cleaned out," he said. Cryptically?

Irene sat two frosty glasses of tea in front of us. "Sure did," she said. A smile? "We got everything put away." Then to me, "We are going to have you stay in Johnny's room. He can't make it home this break. In fact, none of the boys except Jake could make it. Anyway, it took some cleaning up, believe me!"

"Well, looks good," Jake said.

We continued talking. I still suspected nothing when I went upstairs to unpack. Lloyd came home from the university at five-thirty. He sat at the head of the table. He looked a lot like Jake—tall, lean, handsome, thick hair combed to the side.

The next morning I awoke to the smell of bacon and went to the closet to get my robe. Johnny's room had been divided to make an upstairs bathroom, and in the remodeling, a pocket door was fitted in the closet. This morning the door wouldn't budge more than five inches. It felt as if something had fallen on the track. The door made a soft thud when I tried to slide it. I heard Jake's voice in the hall and opened the bedroom door. "Jake, I can't get the closet door open. Is there some trick to it?"

"Let's see." Jake was already dressed in a T-shirt and shorts. I felt suddenly shy in my cotton gown. Jake noticed and smiled lecherously. "Get to work," I said, throwing a pillow.

Jake tried the door. Still blocked. "I'll get Dad," he said. "I think he's awake." He disappeared into his father's room, and in a couple of minutes, they both returned. Lloyd's hair was unruly with sleep, and he was wrapped in a knee-length terry robe. He, too, tried the door.

"Yep!" he said.

"Mother's got coffee ready downstairs," Jake said to me. "Why don't you have some while we work on the door?" He glanced at his father, who was shining a flashlight between the door and wall.

"I need my robe," I said.

"Use mine." Jake ran from the room and returned with a white terry wraparound that smelled like him. He pushed me out the door. As I was going down the stairs, I heard Jake's father's voice. "Be careful."

Irene was already dressed when I entered the kitchen. "Morning!" she said. "Want some coffee?" She had already poured a cup and was pushing it in my direction. There was a pounding in the ceiling directly above us. "What in the world are they up to?" she asked.

"Something's stuck in my closet door," I said, "and it won't open."

She looked at me a moment, but she was thinking of something else. "Oh," she said. Then she told me about when Jake was 12 and broke his ankle building a tree house, which reminded her of the Cub Scouts, which reminded her of the Williamsburg Southern Baptist Church membership drive. After the third cup of coffee, I said I thought I'd see how they were doing. "Why don't you wait down here, hon? You can't get your clothes anyway." Okay. So I waited longer. There was more thumping overhead. A banging. Irene was distracted. Another cup of coffee. I was buzzing. "I'm going up," I said.

I should have waited. I arrived just as Lloyd was pulling a slim five-foot snake from the empty space of the pocket door. "No apparent injuries!" he exclaimed.

At first, I was too stunned to register anything. But instinct caught up with me. I screamed until my throat ached. The snake writhed wildly. Everyone stared at me in shock.

Somehow I ended up in Jake's room. Jake brought my clothes. I shook each thing out several times at arm's length before putting a foot into a pant leg, an arm into a sweater, afraid to find what may still be hidden, more afraid not to. Now, in hindsight, I realize I looked only enough to reassure myself, not enough to become disturbed with what else I might have found. But that is for later.

It was after I ran to the car and Jake followed, trying to console me, that Jake explained his father was a herpetologist.

"A herpetologist?" I asked, a little stunned.

"And he keeps snakes here. In the house. Some of his favorites are often loose. Dad agreed to keep them caged in the storage room during your stay."

"How many more are there?" I asked.

"About twenty-five," Jake answered. "All safely in their aquariums now. Come on back now, Angela, it's safe."

"I'm not going back in," I repeated.

"Angela, they are caged; they won't get out." Jake sounded exasperated.

"No!" I was furious. "How can you be sure that another isn't in a drawer or vent? I'll sleep in the car, but I will not go back into that house."

Jake didn't argue. He packed my clothes while I waited in the car, and then we drove to the motel on the edge of town. Lloyd and Irene politely apologized before we left but withdrew into the house when it became apparent I had no plans of returning.

7

I love to tell this story. I've told it many times—though, for some reason, never to Mama—since it is assured of getting wild laughs, Jake also thinks it is funny, but not as funny as I do. I was sure Mama would love it, but as I told the story, there was only a polite amount of laughter, and by the time I finished, she was staring coldly at Jake. "Loose in the house?" she asked.

I felt instantly defensive for Jake. "Snakes are cleaner than cats," I surprised myself by saying. I surprised her too. And Jake. We all stared at each other in disbelief. What were we talking about?

"Not that I'd have them in the house," I clarified quickly.

"You don't have to tell me that." Jake smirked.

"I never visited Texas," Mama said. "I had an aunt who grew up on a ranch there. It sounded like another world. " She paused. "This, too, California, it is all another world..." Her eyes filled with tears. As I stared into those tears, I saw plains, prairies, checkerboard fields, broken only by tree-lined creeks and splotches of buildings here and there.

Suddenly, I, too, wanted to cry. Had the story worn out, lost its potency? But then it had moved me, not to laughter, but to something more uncomfortable. I felt the ache that comes when something useful and full has come to an end, and as I stared into the distance, I remembered the part of the story I never tell.

Jake and I were driving through darkening streets to the motel. "Angela, the snakes are all in the storage room; they aren't going to get you." He stared straight ahead. He had never been so angry with me.

"Damn, Jake, damn!" I seethed. "There was a fucking five-foot snake in my room when I was sleeping." I started sobbing. Out of rage. Out of fright. He not only had not protected me, he also knowingly colluded in taking me into that!

I could only sob. My world was shifting again. I was afraid to look at Jake, because I was afraid of what else I would see. It was the first time I realized how unlike you Jake was.

8

Of course, I didn't tell the rest of this story to Mama. After we finished our tea, she decided to take a nap. I stayed on the deck. Everyone else was sleeping or busy. Jake and the boys played catch in the park across the street. I heard Trent laughing.

The sounds here are so different from the farm. The rustling of the wind in the madrona and live oak. The popping of Scotch broom pods drying in the sun. The echoing voices of canoeists on the river below. Would this have all seemed strange to you?

Time recedes. In this day of snake stories, another memory comes. You and I are at the snake house at the zoo. Mama waits outside with Dorothy, watching elephants lumber around a denuded corral. Jimmy might be with us, but then again, he's probably racing around by himself. I am holding your large, calloused hand. The place smells like 100 jungles compressed into one gymnasium-size room. The muskiness hurts my nostrils, but I get used to it. A king cobra extends his long, deadly body high up the glass, tongue flickering delicately. Two pythons lie motionless in broken branches. A blue racer moves slowly from its coiled position to a dirty pool. You read each sign to me as I watch.

"King cobra, largest of the venomous snakes.
"African python, considered sacred in parts of Africa.
"Blue racer, most common, quick, and aggressive snake of the Midwestern United States."

I study each serpentine form in this world sealed away, my eyes stinging from the stench of so many snakes too far from the earth.

Again, I felt something surprising shaken out of a familiar story: a pervasive, unsettling sadness. Don't get me wrong: the repulsion and terror were still there. But the serpents suddenly seemed a long way from where they belonged, and I felt myself sickened by more than the memory of the smell.

Perhaps it was time for me to understand snakes.

Plowing

TWO

Oh! serpent, thou who art coiled in my path, get out of my way; for around thee are the mongoose, the porcupine, and the kite in his circles ready to take thee.

Indian snake charmer's chant, Oldfield Howey,
The Encircling Serpent.

1

"Is there anything of your father's you want?" Mama had just come from napping in the room she shared with Kristen. She stood before me as I chopped carrots. The boys were not yet home from day camp, and I was deep in thought. The question caught me off guard.

"I don't know, let me think," I said. My mind raced over objects I've always identified with you. Your flattened hip-pocket wallet. Your thick gold wedding ring. Your worn leather high-topped boots that laced through hooks. I could not think what I'd do with any of these, except the ring, and I knew Jimmy had the ring. "I don't know," I repeated. "Is there anything he wanted me to have?"

"He didn't say." Her voice was low, like it was wearing out. "It all happened so fast. He didn't expect to go." There was a pause. "Of course, the farm will go to you three kids when I am gone. What there is, that is. That farm will never be paid off in my lifetime." She sat on a stool opposite me where the boys often sit when I am cooking.

I'd never presume to ask about her financial affairs, but I said, "Are you all right, Mama? I mean, do you have enough to get by?"

"Oh sure, Angela, don't worry about me. There is social security and some income from the farm, though it is lean these days."

I didn't ask more. I scraped the carrots into an iron kettle and began on the celery. I cut it like she showed me years ago, in narrow strips length wise, and then into tiny cubes.

"You might want his old grade cards," she said.

"His old grade cards?" I didn't know they existed.

"Jimmy found them when he was going through some papers. He also found letters your dad wrote to Grandma during the war and pictures of him, Uncle Will, and Uncle Dan when they were boys. We thought we'd give the letters to Dorothy and divide the pictures between you three. You might want the grade cards." I could tell she was forcing herself to keep talking. Her neck was stiff and businesslike.

"Okay," I said. "Sure."

"And you might want his old chess set. He was quite a chess player when I met him. He even won a state championship. He'd like you to have it, I think."

I never knew you to play chess. But I remember the set from our explorations of the attic. And I'm sure I'll use it more than the old wallet, if it still exists, or the worn leather boots I watched you lace thousands of mornings and noons. Me sitting quietly, chin embedded in my knees, you pulling the leather thongs tight, twisting them under each hook, tying them quickly at the top.

The boys were climbing the back steps to the house. Willie barked his happy dog bark. "Mom!" Wheat yelled. "Maaaa-ommmm!"

I said nothing. Kristen was still sleeping. The gate latch clicked and then the boys were in the kitchen.

"Mom, we got a petition here to get rid …" Wheat began.

"SShhhhh! Kristen is sleeping!" I whispered loudly.

"Oh," he said, more softly. "Mom, we are going to get rid of Ben, the rec teacher. He yelled at another kid today …"

"You mean *you*," Trent added, opening the pantry cupboard.

"and it was the last straw," Wheat continued, undaunted.

"He yelled at you?" I said, carefully. What have my sons been up to?

"Yeah, well, I decided I didn't want to make stupid lanterns. I wanted to learn something the Pomo Indians did, so I told him."

"And he told Wheat that Wheat was a smart aleck and that he would decide what the art projects were, and not some kid ..."

"So I said, okay, if that's how you want it, let's get someone in here who listens to kids..."

"And Wheat almost got expelled from day camp! Mom, you would have been proud of him!" Trent used his sardonic tone that ages him ten years.

"Expelled?" I asked.

"A smart aleck?" Mama said.

"Yeah, Grandma, anyone questions Ben a little, and they're a smart aleck. Real power freak." Wheat grabbed an apple from a bowl on the counter and bit into it loudly.

"He probably put a lot of effort into getting materials ready for those lanterns," Mama said in her now-listen-here tone.

"That's not the point, Grandma," Wheat said. "The point is, he won't listen, and if we criticize, we are smart alecks."

"Your grandson is a revolutionary," Trent quipped, flopping on the stool beside Mama.

She bristled. "So that's what you call it." Her energy was back. "A revolutionary! Sounds more like a smart aleck to me. A teacher is a teacher."

The boys stared at her a moment, then Wheat continued as if she were not there. "Anyway, Mom, we're getting a petition to get Ben fired and half the kids have already signed."

They have more guts than I would have. "I think I'd better call your counselor," I said, "and find out what's going on."

"I told you," Wheat insisted.

Trent ate a slice of raw potato that I was cutting. His skin was golden, his muscular forearms like a man's. "Do you boys want a snack?" I said, pulling the bowl of potato slices away from him.

"Does a bear..." Trent teased.

"Get out of here, both of you," I said. "Take the corn chips and salsa with you."

Mama acted as if she were ignoring what was going on, but I'm sure she remembered every word. I could hear her telling Jimmy. She'd say, "And Angela does nothing about it. Sassy mouths, dirty mouths. And good boys, too. It's not the boys' fault."

2

We, of course, never considered talking back to either you or her when we were kids. To do so was grounds for a spanking when we were young, or a quick slap across the face as we grew older.

The boys took their chips and salsa to the deck. "Maybe that will burn their little tongues out," Mama said.

"What are you saying?" I said angrier than I meant. "Just because they differ with an authority you assume they are wrong?"

"Respect, Angela, respect. We raised you three to respect adults, especially adults in authority."

"I guess we disagree on the definition of respect. Differing with someone doesn't mean you don't respect them."

"In my book, Angela, when a child decides he knows more about how to teach than his teacher, that child is not showing respect for the teacher."

My face burned. "What about respecting the child?" I said. And I remembered standing by the kitchen door thirty years ago, tears leaking, unable to do anything but cry. Was it you, Dad, standing before me? I don't remember the details, but I remember the frustration at being unable to speak. Children do not talk back. "What about respecting the child?" I repeated.

Trent was back. He'd been listening. "Yeah, Grandma, do you want us to not think and be ruled by a bunch of Nazis? Be Nazi meat?"

For a minute I thought she would slap him. "Listen here, Young Man, you may talk to your mother that way, you may talk to your teacher that way, but you are never to talk to me that way!" Wheat appeared at the door, silent. Trent looked confused.

"Mama," I said softly, "the boys are used to saying what they think. That's not disrespectful to us."

Tears flooded her eyes. They flowed over her lids and streamed down her cheeks. "Not where I come from," she said. "Not the way I raised *you*, Angela." She pushed herself back from the counter and got up. She looked frail and spent. "I've got some letters to write," she said. "I think I'll go back to my room."

It was quiet when she left. Wheat stood motionless in the door. Trent fell to a stool. "Sorry," he said.

"Never mind." I start on the onions. "Grandma is having a hard time adjusting to the differences."

"Maybe she's going through the change," Wheat said.

"I think Grandma went through the change many years ago," I said.

"She's a Nazi," Trent said. "I never realized it before."

"She's not a Nazi, Trent, she's just more strict."

"No wonder you moved to California," said Wheat.

"Well, Illinois is a different land, and it was a different time. Families had to be that way. Work had to get done. No questioning about it."

Jake came home in the middle of this. He rubbed Wheat's sandy hair, gave me a kiss, and patted Trent on the back. "Where's Grandma?" he said.

"Crying in Kristen's room," Wheat said.

Jake looked at me.

"Yeah, Dad, I say something intelligent and she just can't take it," Trent said.

"Okay, guys, enough is enough," I said. I put the onions in the pot and added water.

"What's going on?" Jake asked, pulling up the stool Mama was on only minutes before.

"It's complicated," I said. "It started when Wheat and Trent came home saying they're getting a petition to fire Ben the rec teacher, and it went downhill from there."

"Yeah, Dad, he yelled at me today because I didn't want to make lanterns." Wheat pulled up a stool beside Jake.

"And that's why you're getting a petition to get him fired?"

"Well, that is part of it," said Wheat. "He's done nothing but yell since camp started three days ago. And if we say something he doesn't like, he yells more."

"So we're passing around the petition. Half the kids in the camp have already signed and this is only the first day," Trent added. The excitement was building again.

"That doesn't surprise me," said Jake. "Kids love to get back at adults they're angry with. Angela, have you talked with anyone at the camp?"

"When do you think I would have talked with anyone at the camp?" I snapped. "They got home fifteen minutes ago. I'm fixing supper. And we just had the makings of a major riot here." I felt close to tears myself.

"Riot?" Jake asked.

"Yeah, Grandma thinks you should do what teachers say, regardless," Trent said.

And they related the story of how Grandma was a member of a Nazi party terrorizing boys and girls, and that is why I, her daughter, fled to California.

Jake laughed.

"Don't encourage them," I said. "They're getting out of hand on this, and Mama is pretty upset."

"Yeah, well," Jake conceded, and then he turned to Trent. "What time does the camp office close?"

"4:30," Trent answered. "Banker's hours."

"Then I'll drop you off in the morning and see what's up."

"We told you!" Wheat said. "Don't adults believe kids?"

"Cool it, Buddy. I want to hear both sides and then I want it settled."

"And he doesn't want you expelled. Right, Dad?" Trent had that tone again.

"What do you mean expelled?" Jake said.

"For being a smart aleck," Trent explained. Wheat slugged him in the arm.

"Get out of here, boys, out!" I said. They trouped out in mock disgust.

"I'll take them tomorrow," Jake said, getting a beer from the refrigerator and twisting off the cap. I've never drunk beer in front of Mama, and to watch Jake do so makes me choke. Jake, however, does what he wants. "She'll get used to it," he said the first time I mentioned it.

Mama reappeared carrying Kristen who had just awakened from her nap. "Somebody's looking for you," Mama said to me.

I took Kristen to the living room and sat in the rocker tucked away in the corner. Kristen latched onto me ravenously and I felt relieved, at peace with my daughter.

The boys were back. "Oh, good, more chips!" Wheat said.

"Wait a minute, make sure Grandma gets some." Jake pulled the basket from the direction of the boys.

"That's okay, Jake, I'm really not hungry," Mama said. She did not say, I've never eaten chips and salsa in my life, nor do I plan to begin now. "How was your day?" she said in her let's-start-this-over tone.

"Good, Eleanor, good. Busy though. Summer school registration is all this week, and things get real crazy." He took a drink from the dark brown bottle sitting in front of him.

I remembered then how Grandma Galway used to curse those bottles and the poorly lighted places that sold them. "Don't even look

into those places," she told Dorothy and me as we walked past a corner bar in Bloomington.

Mama acted like she didn't notice the bottle.

"Dad," Trent said, standing in front of the open refrigerator, "mind
if I have a beer? I think I'm getting old enough."

I almost died. Then again, maybe I'd murder my sons. At least, I
should tape their mouths shut with sealing tape and lock them up for
the remainder of this visit. Maybe they could go to music camp for
two weeks, one of those camps far away in the high Sierra.

Mama was at the sink getting a drink of water. I couldn't see her
face.

"No, Trent," Jake said.

"Why?" Of course, Trent wasn't going to let this one go.

"Because beer is not for twelve year olds. Or teenagers, for that
matter."

"But you drink it."

"No."

"Double standard!" Trent said. I could see Mama agreed. She
shook her head involuntarily. I could hear her thinking: Set a good
example, not by what you say but what you do.

Jake did not seem perturbed.

Was he enjoying this? Did he enjoy seeing me suffer? Did he think
I was getting my just desserts? Is this what I got because I did not
want to make love last night when he came to bed? I felt him hard
against my thigh, felt his embrace wanting to penetrate me. But I was
not permeable. "No," I said, "Mama might hear." "Across the hall?" he
whispered. "Yes," I said. "It's okay, we're married," he pushed. "No," I
said. "For two weeks? Angela, this is ridiculous." "No," I said. And I
slept feeling untouched, contained, and lonely.

Jake held his calm easy pose. He took another swig from the bottle. The subject changed to an Illinois visit when you took the boys
on a combine. I relaxed and rocked Kristen. She continued nursing
and reached for my mouth. I listened to the newly deepening voice of

Trent, the boyish alto of Wheat, lulled through time to when it was them reaching with those tender baby fingers as I nursed them here. And I remember sitting in this chair, a boy on either thigh, reading, rocking, reading. When was the last time I rocked them? There had to be a last time. Did it go uncelebrated?

3

Since the boys were very young, I have read them mythological stories of our native America. Trent always loved one Zuni story about a beautiful young maiden who continually washed in the sacred pool of Kolowissi the Sea Serpent. She did this because she could not stand dirt or dust on herself or her clothing. Kolowissi did not like his pool dirtied, so he decided to punish her. He changed himself into a baby. When she came the next day, she found the baby, and thinking him abandoned took him home. When she fell asleep, he returned to his serpent form. His coils filled her room. Her father bargained with Kolowissi to release his daughter, but she had to give herself to the Serpent and go live in his house of the Sacred Waters. The maiden bid her people goodbye and walked away burdened by the heavy head of the enormous Serpent on her shoulder. Kolowissi was so long that even after the maiden had walked many miles with his head on her shoulder, the snake still wasn't completely uncoiled from her room. Eventually Kolowissi abandoned his snake form and changed into the figure of a brave young man. The maiden wouldn't speak to him, however, because of her fear and shame. But she did listen to him and soon learned he was the Sea Serpent, that he loved her too much to return her to her people, and that they would live in the Waters of the World. As she followed her husband, she forgot her sadness and her home and she lived with him ever after.

"Lived with a snake!" Trent used to say. "She married a snake?"

"Kolowissi is a god," I'd explain. "He can take any form. But his favorite is that of a serpent."

"She forgot her family?" Trent asked.

"Well, she went on without them."

"But why did she have to leave?"

"All children leave eventually," I'd say, hugging him, "when they're ready. She had to. She dirtied the sacred waters and she had to pay."

"By marrying a snake?"

"It was her fate."

"What is fate, Mom?"

"The natural result of how things go. Like, if you are too clean, your fate may be to put up with the dirt and not dirty up someone else's water trying to be too clean."

"Oh," Trent said. "Oh well. At least he turned into a brave young man."

"Yeah, " I said, "but he was still a sea serpent inside."

4

It rained the day you helped me pack the Volvo to drive to California. It rained so hard in the afternoon we had to pull the car into the garage. You changed the oil and checked the water in the radiator and battery while I stacked boxes of ceramic plates and books, jewelry, and scarves smelling faintly of Here's My Heart along the garage wall. I lugged suitcases packed with underwear, jeans, and heavy sweaters, as well as a brown plaid skirt that went with every sweater I owned. I might need it for work.

You were silent as you slammed the hood. You wiped your hand on a thick pink rag. We did not make eye contact. The garage felt as swollen as my throat.

"I wish you had kept the Ford," you said. "If you have car trouble on the road, no one can fix a Volvo."

"I won't have car trouble, Dad." My voice sounded reassuring though foolhardy, I think now. "I just had it serviced. The old Volvo is in good shape."

"I hope so," you replied. I wanted to believe that is what you hoped, and yet I didn't. I knew you would love to come rescue me. I could picture myself stranded in Kansas. I'd use the dime tucked in between my billfold pictures you'd given me years before for dates.

Dad, I'm in Topeka, Kansas. The Volvo is making a bumping noise. Will you come pick me up? Your response would be predictable. I'll be right there, you'd say. And I'd wait in my car until you pulled up, Mama beside you, your face relaxed and calm and welcome.

But that day your face was set as I was so used to seeing it over the years when you had a long task to do, and you were going to complete it. I saw the expression at the end of each row as you were plowing. It wasn't a bored expression. It was an elsewhere expression, a keep going expression, a resigned expression. You were turning now. Reposition the plow. Put the tractor in low. Move slowly ahead.

You opened my car door. "This isn't all going to fit," you said. "We'll have to take things out of the boxes." So I unpacked the boxes, except for the dishes and books, while you placed the box of dishes on the back seat and stuffed towels and sheets around it to protect it from the jarring of the car. You put my jewelry box under the front seat, and wrapped the tiny perfume bottles in newspaper and stuffed them inside the dishes. The pile outside the car grew smaller as the Volvo sunk lower and lower on its wheels. We worked in silence. When you climbed out of the back, the car jumped. You looked at what was left, the box of paperbacks and notebooks, the pillow and blankets, a suitcase. The walls of the garage swelled with the dampness. We did not look at each other. I imagine you readjusted the bill of your cap. Raise the plow, turn, reposition the plow, and move forward.

The box of books fit neatly on the floor of the front seat. The suitcase fit on the passenger seat. I lay the pillow on top of that, but you tucked it away in the back. "Won't obstruct the view," you said.

The tires were flatter. You backed the car within reach of the air compressor and added air to each tire. Fft! Fft!..Fft! Fft! The garage was chilly in spite of the August afternoon. I did not find the familiar grease smell comforting. I fought back shadows of Jimmy and Dorothy and me exploring this garage not that many years ago. Jimmy'd lead us up the ladder at the far end of the garage and into the loft. The world swelled then too, but it was with mystery dampened with the firm hold of chores to be done in an hour or our mother's watchful eye. There was promise, but it was in what was not seen. We were safe. "Jimmy! Angela! Time to set the table!" We knew we couldn't sail too far. We knew the perimeters. "Angela! Bring Dorothy in for her nap!" And we would return to the order, the neatly manicured lawn, the house sweet with meatloaf and ivory soap. Our mothers and fathers reeled us in, so we did not go too far.

I know if I considered this too much, this grease and garage dampness, I would not leave. I collected my maps and placed them on the dashboard. I wiped the rearview mirror with a paper towel. Turn, reposition, forward.

And so you prepared me for my maiden voyage. You packed my vessel with those items I would need in the other world. "I'll be back in six months," I said, "when the semester is over. I'll be back in the spring."

You were silent. My voice was rusty. Somewhere in a far corner, something was gnawing.

5

"Angela, we've got a problem here." Jake's voice was businesslike. I was dripping. I clasped a thin terry towel about me. The morning sun blared through the skylight of the hallway illuminating a universe of dust motes. I wondered how we could even breathe as I stood there interrupted from my shower, talking to Jake on the phone.

"Oh?" I said, acting like what in the world can it be? But I knew. I feared this. How many times have I received calls from the school?

Calls that pull me from my weaving, or make me lay Kristen down as she pops away from my breast, or force me to turn the burner off so the sauteing onions do not turn into black, curled worms. How many times have I heard the no-nonsense tone on the other end of the phone? "Mrs. Tyler? There has been a problem today with your son, can you come for a teacher's conference, now?"

So I had expected this call. "Wheat won't stay," Jake said. "The camp is taking a hard line to his objections, so there is a complete standoff. This is camp, not school. I think he might as well come home. This one isn't worth fighting."

"Okay." Each time it is different. Wheat has questioned a homework assignment, or he has protested the care of a chameleon in the science room. "Okay, do you want me to pick him up, or do you have time to bring him back?"

"Would you get him? I need to be at a meeting at ten, and I'm short on time as it is."

"Sure," I said, mentally rearranging the morning.

"Thanks," Jake said. "I've got to go." The phone clicked.

Wheat was waiting in the shade of a madrone. His fingers were wrapped in pieces of peeled bark so they looked like claws. "Hi, Grandma, Hi, Mom," he said as he slid into the back seat beside Kristen. Kristen cooed a greeting. "Hello, Leech." He poked one of his claws into her belly. I could see him in the rear view mirror. "Don't let her get those claws in her mouth," I said.

The air was tense. "Did Dad tell you what they said?"

"No, we'll talk about it this evening. He just said it was okay for you to come home."

Wheat let out a sigh and leaned back. "That camp is full of Nazis. No offense, Grandma."

Mama swung around in the seat to face him. "What are you talking about, Young Man?" I felt sick.

"I thought you liked Nazis," Wheat said seriously. "Out here they are bad people, but maybe in Illinois they aren't so bad."

Mama looked at me. I checked the rear view mirror. Wheat stared back earnestly.

"We aren't going to discuss this now," I said. "We are taking an excursion to Fort Ross."

Wheat leaned back in his seat again. Mama looked straight ahead. Kristen cooed.

"Why are we going to Fort Ross?" Wheat asked after a respectful pause.

"To see the fort," I said.

"Would you drop me off at home?"

"Alone?"

"I'll call Ian. Or maybe Dustin. They are home this week."

Our eyes met in the rear view mirror. "No, we are already off to a late start. Besides, you like Fort Ross."

"But I don't like the ride there. It makes me car sick."

"We'll be off this windy road soon."

"And then onto another," Wheat moaned.

"You should have stayed at camp," Mama said.

I feel my shoulders tighten. "Why?" Wheat asked.

"Then you wouldn't be car sick." She stared straight ahead as she said this. It was a familiar pose. It gave her an air of advantage.

But it didn't work on Wheat the way it does on me. He looked at me in the rear view mirror like he thought she was crazy.

I ignored this. "Let up on Wheat," I said.

"You think I'm hard on him?"

"Yes."

"He gets kicked out of camp for insubordination and then wants to be driven around at his orders and you think I'm hard on him?"

"He wasn't kicked out. He didn't want to be there, and we didn't force him."

"I know it's none of my business," she said, "but you have to be careful letting kids run the show."

"So you think we're letting him run the show!" My voice was raising. Wheat sat up again in his seat.

"Yes!" she said triumphantly.

There are some things I do not say. I do not say them because I've never said them, to her or to you. I lowered my voice. "Mama, Wheat is not running the show. Jake and I decided this one wasn't worth pushing." She wasn't looking at me. I could see her out of the corner of my eye. She looked out the right passenger window at a landscape she had never seen until this week. Her face was thinner, harsher, more bone than it was in the days I knew her, that other mother larger than life, the one I never questioned. If my son were not so stubborn, if he were at camp now, if my sons did not say what they think and fight for the right to do so, would her face become fuller, the hollows under her eyes swell, until she was the mother I knew on that cultivated prairie? And yet, I remember her this way too, standing rigid in the doorway of Dorothy's and my room. "Girls, go to sleep!" Her silhouette threatened if we did not calm our giggles. Sometimes she lingered a moment too long, until our laughs escaped us making horrible snorts in the silence. It was all over then. We knew it the minute the sound penetrated the air. There was the quick movement to my bed, the expected swat, the movement to Dorothy's bed, and the swat muffled in bed covers. As our giggles became cries, *Oh, Mama, don't!*, she left saying, "Don't make me come back in here again!" And we didn't. It was the other part of feeling safe. We knew the limits. When we trespassed, we were punished in prescribed ways, so we did not become bold, belligerent children.

We reached Highway One and turned right. The Russian River paralleled us on our left with wide, grassy meadows as banks. I noticed we were low on gas, so I stopped at the filling station in Jenner. Wheat said he had to pee, and Mama flinched. As Wheat disappeared into the station, she stepped out of the car and stretched. I closed the car door quietly as I got out so as not to awaken Kristen. The day was unusually warm. Gulls flapped silver wings overhead, squawking.

"Sea gulls!" Mama said.

"Yes," I said, happy to have something neutral to talk about. I shoved the nozzle into the tank of my car.

Wheat returned. "Hey, Grandma, look, there's an osprey!" He pointed excitedly to a bird high above the widening river. The bird flapped its wings up and down in characteristic osprey fashion. "We have an osprey tree near us," he continued. "They come back to the same nest every year."

Mama thought Wheat was making up to her. "How do you know so much about birds?" she asked, putting an arm around his shoulder.

Wheat studied the bird as he answered. "Dad. And camp. Last year we had counsellors who were more interested in teaching us something than in bossing us around."

The gas nozzle clicked. Mama looked at Wheat, her arm frozen millimeters above his shoulder. "Get in the car, Wheat," I said. "Time to get going."

"Okay, Mom, okay."

Mama got in the front as I handed the attendant my credit card. I leaned against the left rear fender, watching him stamp the receipt. I took a breath of salt air before I got back into the car.

It was quiet. "Get ready for some spectacular scenery," I said.

"Yeah, cars go off the side all the time. Drunks' cars, that is." Wheat looked at me innocently in the rear view mirror.

Mama looked at the slope of Jenner with its scattered hillside homes. The sky was blue as the sea, which we could see straight ahead. "This is just beautiful, Angela!" she said.

"I love the ocean," I said, feeling shy. "I never saw this sea until I was twenty, and now I can't imagine living far from it."

"Especially with Dad," said Wheat.

"Well, that's another reason," I added, steering around the curve that took us out of Jenner and away from the river's mouth. As long as Jake teaches marine biology, we'd have a hard time moving.

"Angela, this is just beautiful!" Mama repeated. Ahead of us stretched miles of white capped rocky shoreline.

"Just wait 'til we get to the place the drunks go off," said Wheat. "It's straight down, hundreds of feet. No railing either."

Mama looked uncomfortable. Wheat had obviously forgotten his car sickness. He was peering out the window above Kristen, checking to see how high we were above the surf.

"Do you have drunks in Illinois?" I felt my neck stiffen.

"Oh, of course, Wheat, they just don't have cliffs to drive off."

This tickled Wheat. He laughed, relaxed, and pulled himself forward to rest on the back of the front seat. "Wasn't Mom's grandpa an alcoholic?" I almost braked and turned in my seat to say, now listen here, Young Man, but didn't. My neck stiffened more instead.

"Good heavens, no!" Mama said. "Whatever gave you that idea?"

"Mom," Wheat answered. "She said her dad told her grandpa used to get so drunk during threshing time the men had to help him up the walk when he went home."

"Well, that may be true, but it was before I knew your grandpa."

"So does that make him an alkie?"

"Angela, where does he get these words?"

"Drug education in the schools. They just did a unit on family patterns of alcoholism." The old we-studied-it-in-school trick.

"Well, the best way to prevent alcoholism is to not drink," Mama said. "Your grandpa never drank a drop." She turned to face Wheat.

"Dad drinks and he's not a drunk." My heart sank. When did my sons become so brave? Or is it that they never lost it? Was I ever this way? Or was I born with a thermostat that clinches my neck and shuts me off when things heat up.

"No, he's not a drunk, but if you don't drink, you can't become a drunk," she reiterated. "And if you do, you can."

This continued for ten more miles up the windy coast, around cliffs that dropped into a pounding surf, through pastures with sheep paths leading straight up and straight down, and finally, into the rolling

meadows of Fort Ross. I had a headache when we arrived. Wheat
bounded out of the car, stretching, then raced to find a water fountain.
Kristen awakened and made fussy grunts. I unlatched her from her
car seat, then nursed her in the driver's seat. Mama sat beside me.

I watched white capped waves rushing for a shore I couldn't see.
My shoulders relaxed as my eyes closed. Mama knitted. I heard her
needles click-clicking, click-clicking, pulsating, beating...

Again, I thought of you. You would have slapped me if I acted as
Wheat had. Again I saw myself in the kitchen, tears blurring my vi-
sion. "Do not talk back." What had happened? It was probably something simple. I wanted to play, you wanted me to help Mama with
the dishes. Had I said no? I felt fire inside, leaping up, exploding into
flame. "Don't look at me like that, Young Lady!" you boomed. And
then there was a stinging slap on the side of my face.

6

"I wonder what that child is up to?" Mama said. Several minutes
had passed.

"Hard to say. He knows the Fort pretty well."

"Well, boys will be boys," she said. I suppose it was to excuse his
independence.

I said nothing. I closed my eyes again and leaned my head against
the headrest. Kristen continued nursing. Then you were standing before me, and I was sobbing. "Don't ever look at me that way again,"
you say. "There's more where that came from."

"Mom! Maaa..ommmm!"

"Shhhhh!" I motioned, though everyone else was alert. Kristen's
eyes widened as she watched Wheat approach. She was still attached
with the suction of an abalone.

"Mom!" Wheat said, more quietly, "There's a storyteller here! He's
a gypsy from someplace in France. He speaks four languages and tells

stories in three." His eyes were as wide as Kristen's. I'd never noticed a resemblance between them before.

"Just a few minutes," I said. "We'll be right there. Where is he?"

"Near the old well." Wheat looked at Mama. "Grandma, do you want to come with me?"

"Sure," she said, putting down her knitting. I watched them go up the path to the visitor's center, she in her blue polyester knit slacks and white shell, grey curly hair circling her head, and Wheat, not quite as tall but lean and gangly, with knees and feet to grow into. I could hear Wheat's excited voice as they walked off. Words drifted back to me. "Gypsy...tour...hitchhike...tent" and then I felt my eyes droop and I started dreaming that Wheat ran off with the circus.

Kristen brought me back when she squirmed abruptly. She'd finished nursing. I changed her diapers in the front seat, grabbed the sack of sandwiches and soft drinks Mama packed that morning, and pushed Kristen in her stroller to the Fort. When I entered the stockade, I saw a scattering of people around a bearded man making exaggerated movements with his hands. They sat in the center of the squared stockade, near the log fence that enclosed the well. Mama stood in the back. She waved to me and I pushed the stroller through the grass to the well. Wheat was in front. He briefly acknowledged me with a glance.

"I need some helpers for this next story I am going to tell," the storyteller said. Several hands shot up like flags. He quickly chose two girls and a small boy. "Now we need a snake! And not just any old snake, either, no, this is the first snake, the great primordial boa!" He scanned the audience a couple of seconds, and then pointed to Wheat. "You!" he said. "You will make a good primordial boa." Wheat walked to the front, obviously pleased with his role. "Now one more," the storyteller said. "We need the primordial boa's child, Olodumare. ...Ah, you!" He pointed to a frail looking girl with limp blonde hair who didn't have her hand up. The girl hid her face and shook her head. "Oh, come, now," said the storyteller, "we have work to do. We are about to create the world." The girl took her place in front with the rest of the group.

"This story comes from Africa, like all the stories I'll be telling today," said the storyteller, mostly to the adults in the back. "It was told to me by a very old Yoruba man as we sat in his dark hut."

"So! We have a snake, the great primordial boa, and we have his child, Olodumare." He assigned the roles of chameleon to the boy and pigeon and five-toed hen to the girls.

"We are ready now." He stood up straight and tossed his chin length hair back as he cleared his throat. "Ladies and gentlemen! For reasons I do not know, the great primordial boa," he motioned to Wheat, who bowed deeply, "decided to send his child," he gestured toward Olodumare, who stared foolishly at the ground, "to the watery wastes to create the world! Olodumare...Olodumare, get your helpers, the five-toed hen and pigeon.... Olodumare sent her helpers to the wastes with a packet of earth." A small packet of earth magically appeared in his hand, and he handed it to Olodumare who in turn shyly passed it on to the five-toed hen. "The five-toed hen and the pigeon were to take the earth and scratch and spread it about to make a world wide and dry enough for other creatures to live on." The hen and pigeon dumped the packet of earth and scratched it about with their feet. Were the first laborers of creation farmers, I wondered?

"Great," said the storyteller, "keep it up until you think the earth is wide enough."

Dirt clouds rose. "Okay," said the five-toed hen, "it's done!"

"Now," the storyteller said to Olodumare, "direct your chameleons to go down and check the work."

"Check the work," Olodumare ordered the chameleon, who must have been her brother.

So the chameleon crawled to the scratching site, the storyteller beside him. "Looks pretty good, huh?" said the storyteller. "Good and wide... but, oh, no, it's so wet it's like quicksand!" The group laughed wildly as the storyteller appeared to sink in the mud. "Go tell Olodumare there's a lot of land, but it's too muddy!"

The chameleon relayed the message, and after a wait and a second visit, he reported to Olodumare it was wide and dry enough. And Olodumare said, "Oh, good."

"Now animals can live on the earth safely," the storyteller said. "It didn't happen overnight either. No, it took five days to create the world. I think Olodumare even moved down to earth. And you know what that old boa did when Olodumare moved away from the heavens? Now, I can't give you all the details, because it isn't nice, but," he put an arm around Wheat and pulled him forward, "but he wanted Olodumare to remember him, so he put out his magical snake excrement and today you can see its reflection when you see a rainbow. If you collect just a little, it will make you wealthy and prosperous! And that is the end of this story! Or the beginning, whichever."

"That story was pornographic," Mama said. Kristen began to fuss. The kids called for another story. "Let's walk through the stockade and let Wheat stay here," I said, gesturing to the log buildings.

Kristen quieted when the stroller was moving again. Mama and I toured the log replicas of buildings the Russians built 150 years ago when they moved here to hunt sea otters and plant grains, vegetables, and fruit trees. We were eating sandwiches on the benches beside the officers' quarters when the storytelling crowd dispersed. Wheat ran toward us.

"Mom!" he yelled. "Mom! Do you have any money?"

"Why do you need money?" I asked as he got closer.

"For the storyteller! That's how he earns his living. He tells stories and people give him money."

I reached for my purse, found my billfold, and handed him a dollar.

"Only a dollar?" His eyes were round with disbelief. "What can you get for a dollar?"

"Okay, give him two then." I handed him another bill.

"Only two dollars?" Wheat gasped. "What can you ..."

"Did you bring your allowance?" I interrupted. "If you want to give him more, use your own money."

Wheat turned to Mama. "Grandma?"

"Certainly not!" she snapped. "I do not support hobos!" She wiped her fingers on a paper towel.

"He's not a hobo, Grandma, he's a storyteller," Wheat replied, outraged, "an artist!"

"If he wants money, let him work for it like the rest of us." She turned to me. "Really, Angela, what are you teaching him giving him money to support this tramp?"

"He's not a tramp, Grandma!"

"Wheat," I said, wanting to get this over with, "get going! We need to leave in a few minutes so we are back before Trent gets home."

As Wheat sped off, I gathered up the garbage, stuffing the paper towel and aluminum cans into a paper sack. When Wheat returned, he was not alone.

"Mom, this is Jean-Pierre! He needs a place to camp tonight, so I offered him our garden."

It was, of course, the storyteller. He was larger than he looked in the middle of the stockade. His dark brown hair had a windblown look even though the air was absolutely still, and his smile was comical, quizzical. "Bonjour, Madame!" he said, extending a smooth, though strong, hand.

"Hello," I said.

"And this is my grandma," Wheat continued, turning to Mama. "She's from Illinois, and she's not used to storytellers."

Mama must have been getting used to Wheat. She looked him in the eye a long second before turning to the storyteller and offering her hand. "Hello," she said in her most polite voice.

"Wheat," I said, "You could hardly call our garden a very good place to camp... it is really more of a thicket."

"Mom thinks of it as a snake pit," Wheat said to Jean-Pierre. "She thinks it is a jungle and every snake in the country was born there."

I gave Wheat a kick-under-the-table look. Jean-Pierre did not seem to notice.

"I've camped in places not so nice as yours, I'm sure." His voice was musical with its gentle French accent. "I'm grateful for your kind offer."

I smiled automatically. I can't remember why I was going to object. "You are welcome to our thicket," I said. I felt Mama's stare.

"First I must talk with the ranger before we leave," he said.

"He's on foot, Mom, and he needs a ride."

It was going faster than I planned. "Meet you at the car," I said.

Wheat was exuberant. His knees had springs as he bounced off with Jean-Pierre.

I turned to Mama before she had a chance to speak. "Let's take the long trail back to the parking lot," I said.

"Angela, that man could be a rapist!" she said when we were out of earshot.

"He's not though. He knows the rangers."

"He's a gypsy, Angela, that's who lives in France. Gypsies! And gypsies can't be trusted, not one of them. They come to your door with some scrawny baby, begging for milk, and when you go to get it for them, they take your tomatoes, right off the porch!"

"That was in Illinois, Mama, and it was during the depression."

"What will Jake say?" she demanded. "You pick up a tramp when you have children in the car."

I tried not to think. "He trusts my judgment," I said.

"Angela, you are far too lax. You always were." But she almost sounded relieved. This was something that hadn't changed. Then she laughed unexpectedly. "Maybe he'll tell some good stories," she said. I looked at her and grinned. She shook her head in resignation.

There is nothing more level than the ocean that stretched before us, unless it is the prairie. We were quiet as the path led us toward the watery expanse. As we passed thick-trunked eucalyptus trees that had dropped silvered tops and brown buttons on the path, Mama collected several handfuls, stuffing them into the pockets of her pants. I walked a pacifying pace, keeping Kristen moving, but not getting too far ahead of Mama. She kept staring out to sea.

"Wouldn't it be something to have an ocean in your backyard?" she said. That day it did seem quiet enough to be a part of a backyard. "I can't smell the earth though."

"It's probably the eucalyptus," I said. "It takes over."

"No," she said. "I can smell the ocean, the coolness, the salt, but even in all this sun I can't smell dirt. I'd miss that." Her eyes became liquid.

"I guess you'd get used to these other smells," I said. "The ocean, the pennyroyal, the eucalyptus." I handed her a particularly pungent brown button to smell.

"Whoof!" she gasped. "That smells like a cough drop!"

I'd never thought of it that way. In fact, I thought of it as the smell I try to weave into my greens, that frosts them with salt and cools them until they are part water and part earth.

As Kristen grew impatient, her stewing fuss escalated into a full blown cry. I picked her up. She immediately stopped and bit my cheek, then my shoulder. "Wait till we get to the car," I said.

"With the hobo?" Mama said. "No, Angela, you are not going to nurse that child with a strange man in the car. Let's stop over here."

I did not remind her that the picnic tables she had pointed out were public property and that any lecher or rapist could find us there. And I did not object. I carried Kristen to a bench, sat down, and let her nurse. She was not very hungry, however, and in five minutes we were back on the path to the parking lot.

Wheat and Jean-Pierre were waiting for us at the car. A large backpack leaned against the passenger side back door. "What took you so long," Wheat greeted us.

"Suddenly you're in a hurry," I replied.

"I want Trent to meet Jean-Pierre." Jean-Pierre was wisely quiet and humble.

I unlocked the doors and then the trunk. "Let's see if we can fit the pack in here," I said to Jean-Pierre. He deftly maneuvered it into the space, then closed the trunk and opened my door for me. "Thanks," I say.

"*Merci*, Mom, *merci*. That's French for thanks."

7

At least on the drive back Mama and Wheat did not spar. Mama was silent except for the times she looked out the right passenger window and exclaimed, "How could they ever have built a road here!" Then I knew she had one of those vertical views of steep slopes covered with grass the color of Wheat's hair and sheep trails looping up the sides like leis on a Christmas tree.

Wheat, though, questioned Jean-Pierre incessantly, and Jean-Pierre answered with all the charm of... a con man? Was this my mother's voice? I found him entertaining and I did believe him when he said he'd just come from Africa where he'd exchanged stories with the Yoruba tribesmen. But the discomfort. Was it like Mama who feels disoriented when she cannot smell the earth? This man was the wind and traveled with it, unrooted, gracious, dependent on the whims of his listeners and acquaintances.

Trent was home when we got there. He had an enormous bowl of ice cream with chocolate syrup smothering it and was lounging on the deck, feet on the table. "Where've ya been?" he greeted me. He sounded like Jake.

"Fort Ross," I said.

"This is my brother," Wheat said, coming down the steps behind me not more than two feet from Jean-Pierre. Then he saw the bowl. "Hey, Mom, Trent's got ice cream. Can Jean-Pierre and I have some?"

"It's gone," Trent stated.

"Mom, that's not fair. He ate all the ice cream."

"Get a sandwich," I said. " Supper's going to be late."

"I want ice cream!" Wheat said. Then remembering Jean-Pierre, he added, "Oh, so much for my brother, the Pig, let's get something and I'll show you the garden." He looked at Trent importantly as he went to the kitchen.

"*Bonjour,* Trent," Jean-Pierre said in his winning voice. He held out a hand.

Trent put his feet on the ground, set his bowl on the table, and shook Jean-Pierre's hand. "Hi," he answered, shyly. Wheat came out of the kitchen with a bag of chips and two Cokes. "Come on, Jean-Pierre, I'll show you where to put up your tent." They went down the garden steps.

Trent turned to me. "Mom, who is that!"

"Jean-Pierre," I said. "A storyteller."

"But how did he get here?"

"Wheat invited him."

"From where?" He sounded more like Jake every day.

"The Fort."

"You mean you picked up a stranger at the Fort?"

"That boy has good sense," said Mama. She was sitting in the chair beside Trent, holding Kristen. "That's just what I said, Trent."

"Listen," I said, "I know this is not usual, but he's only *sleeping* in the garden. We did not invite him to sleep in your room or on the sofa. And, he's nice."

Wheat and Jean-Pierre came back up. "Mom," Wheat called, "Jean Pierre wants to take a shower. Can he use your bathroom?"

"Have him use the downstairs one."

"But it's so small."

"Mine has clothes drying in it," I said. "Get Jean-Pierre a towel from your linen closet." They went into the house.

"He's just going to use the garden, huh?" Trent said.

"The garden, the bathroom, and anything else he can get away with," Mama piped in. "Watch your tomatoes, Angela!"

8

Jake met Jean-Pierre with his hair dripping from the shower. "*Bonjour, Monsieur,*" Jean-Pierre greeted him. "I am camping in your garden."

"*Bonjour,*" Jake replied, looking at me. As Jean-Pierre descended to the garden, Jake came to me.

"Wheat found him today at Fort Ross," I explained before he could say a word. "He needed a place to camp tonight. He's a storyteller."

"What?" Jake said.

"That's exactly what I thought," said Mama. "Angela picked up a hobo and brought him home. She's always been this way, Jake. Well, all I can say is, protect your valuables."

I gave Mama a dirty look and returned to the kitchen. Jake followed. "He's a storyteller from Fort Ross," I said.

"In our garden, Angela? What's gotten into you?"

"It wouldn't have been my first choice," I said, more strongly now, "but now I can see it's not a bad choice. He's really interesting." I trimmed the fat from the last pork chop and fit it in the skillet to brown with the others. Jake doesn't make decisions like I do. He never has. Decisions happen to me. Jake and Mama think of this as being a pushover, and I'm sure you did too. I think of it as living on the edge. Things happen that I could never conceive of on my own.

"Have you invited him to dinner?" Jake asked, counting the chops.

"No," I said, "but you can bet Wheat will."

Mama brought Kristen in from the deck. "What can I help you with," she asked.

By dinner Trent was as taken by Jean-Pierre as Wheat was. All three were in the garden. Jake had to go get them. Jean-Pierre, of course, joined us and we had an enchanted conversation about his travels in Africa. Toward the end of the meal, Wheat suggested Jean-Pierre use the sofabed in the living room. Jean-Pierre politely declined, saying he loved to sleep under the stars.

"But you're not sleeping under the stars, you're sleeping in a tent!" Wheat persisted.

"Ah yes, but the tent has a window," Jean-Pierre said, "and the things I can see from that window!"

"Mom thinks the garden is full of snakes," Trent said. "She won't even go into it."

"It won't be the first time I sleep with snakes," Jean-Pierre said, folding his napkin and putting it on his empty plate.

"You slept with snakes?" Wheat said.

"In Africa," Jean-Pierre said. "In Africa they do not stop the python from entering. They say he is sacred. I was sleeping on the floor of the kind gentleman who told me the story of the primordial boa and Olodumare. I felt this lump..."

"Oh no!" I said.

"That's what happens!" Mama said.

"And I thought, oh, a rock. But the lump moved."

"What did you do then," Wheat asked.

"I shined my flashlight on it. Sure enough. A four foot snake as big around as my arm."

"Oh Jesus," I said.

"What did you do then," Trent asked.

"What did it look like," Wheat asked simultaneously.

"Oh please, one question at a time!" Jean-Pierre laughed. "I don't remember exactly what it looked like. Big. Snakey. And what I did was, I moved my pad! In Africa you do not bother the snake."

"Healthy approach," said Jake.

"Yeah, well, you've probably had several snakes under your mattresses," I said.

"And you may have too," he taunted back.

"Vera lives in the garden," Wheat said.

"Who's Vera?" asked Jean-Pierre.

"A garter snake," Trent explained.

"For Mom, the great primordial boa," said Wheat. "You never know where you'll find Vera. Sometimes she's under the deck. Sometimes she's lying in the sun. Sometimes she's hiding in the baby tears."

"Uncle Wilmar ran into a snake as big around as a man's arm once," Mama said. "Did I ever tell you boys about the time he went to collect the eggs?"

"No," Trent said.

"What happened?" Wheat asked.

"Well, it was getting dark and Uncle Wilmar's mother gave him an egg basket and told him to gather the eggs. He went into the hen house to the straw-filled bins. There was no electricity in those days, so hen houses were one of the darkest places on earth. He could barely see the white of the eggs. He collected all the eggs in the top bins, but when he got to the bottom row, he came to a bin that was especially dark inside. Something told him not to put his hand in there. He lit the kerosene lantern, showed it on the nest, and sure enough, there was a great big timber rattler!"

"What did he do?" Trent asked.

"He got his mother, who was an excellent markswoman, and she shot its head off. They say that snake was five feet long."

"I didn't realize there were rattlesnakes around Flat Rock," I said.

"Once there were a lot," Jake said, "before the early settlers killed them."

"Poor snakes!" Wheat said, his voice full of emotion.

"Poor snakes, nothing!" said Mama. "Do you have any idea what would have happened if Uncle Wilmar put his hand into that nest?"

"He shouldn't put his hand into dark places," said Trent.

"That's what the Indians did," Wheat said. "They didn't kill rattlers. They called them grandfather and learned to live with them."

Mama looked at me.

"Jake's influence," I shrugged.

9

The storyteller left at sunrise the next day. I was the only one who saw him go. I had risen early, as you always did, to savor the quiet of the house. Slipping from the warm covers smelling of Jake and breast milk, I left Kristen limp with dreams beside her daddy, and crept to the window. I could see his tent in the garden. The fog inched up the river like a giant furry caterpillar. It's going to be hot, I thought. The sky is crystalline, and it's going to be hot.

He emerged from his tent then, naked in the dawn light, first his head and broad shoulders, then his muscular torso, hips, and legs. Apollo could not have been more beautiful. As I watched, he stretched and then peed in some bushes, his back to me. I took care not to be seen as I watched him pull on his jeans and zip his fly. Which makes me think of you again, though you would have been scandalized had you ever caught me watching you dress. Of course, I never had the opportunity.

I decided to weave until the others woke. Remembering the first time I saw a man nude, I sat down to my loom. I did not move when I heard the storyteller push what I assumed was a note under the kitchen doorjamb. Instead, I chose a piece of burgundy yarn to splice into the browns of my weaving. That day so long ago, Jimmy and I had convinced Uncle Dan to take us fishing with him. We had never gone before, although we knew about his afternoon trips to the Sangamon river. The evenings after these trips, he'd have a fish fry. We kids ran through the barns and over the close cropped grass of Uncle Dan's yard until fireflies flickered and our sweat made us chilly. Then our mothers would tell us to get sweaters, and we would sit while you grown-ups finished talking around the long church tables set up on the lawn.

This particular trip I had just turned ten. I remember because Uncle Dan said you had to be ten to catch catfish. Jimmy and I rode with Charley in the back of Uncle Dan's pickup. Charley's Uncle Hershel was also coming. Hershel was a medium-sized, tanned man with no shirt sleeve lines on his arms and with hands as clean as a woman's. Charley said he was a pharmacist who worked in Springfield. Jess White and Bill Daniels drove another pickup filled with nets, buckets, and other gear. All the men were wearing bibbed overalls and no shirts. We kids wore our old swimming suits because Mama wouldn't let us wear our new ones in muddy river water.

The day began quietly. The men unloaded the truck, letting us kids swim while they worked. River swimming was new to me. Mama had always said river currents were unpredictable. She said even the best of swimmers could suddenly get sucked down and drown. We usually swam in the chlorinated pool at the Y, but this day you convinced her to let Jimmy and me go with Uncle Dan. "It's safe where Dan goes," you told her.

River water smells alive and goes on forever. As I eased into the cool, forbidden fluid, tiny ripples reflected a world hidden from me on the farm. Here, I could lie on an innertube and float aimlessly with the mild current through an alley of willows and fishing camps that I never knew existed. Each time we disappeared from his sight, Uncle Dan called, "Back this way, kids!" and we would race each other upstream.

I remember the men standing across the width of the river with the net stretched from one to another. Their wet overalls hung heavy from their strong shoulders. They used gloves to grab and toss the big snouted catfish into large galvanized tubs on the bank.

It happened shortly after Uncle Dan called us back the third time. We were swimming upstream on our stomachs, pushing the innertubes ahead of us, splashing each other with our kicking. The river was thick and dark and smooth. In the shallow places where we had to stand, mud oozed between our toes.

It is not that I thought snakes didn't live in rivers. I knew they did. In Girl Scouts we had seen snakes sunning themselves on low willow branches, dropping into the water at our approach. I just did not think about it, as if this would protect me.

The urgency of Uncle Dan's voice caused us three kids to stop and stare, dumbstruck. "Hershel, I'll get it!" There was Hershel, stiff, holding the head of a large brown water snake a foot from his face. The writhing snake had somehow gotten into his overalls. He didn't scream because he couldn't. Instead he tottered and fell backwards into the waist deep water, still holding the snake's head.

The next thing I remember I was standing on the bank. Jimmy and Charley rushed toward Hershel but Uncle Dan waved them away. "Get back, kids," he shouted, pulling the overall suspenders from Hershel's shoulders. Jess dragged Hershel to the bank. Hershel was still holding the snake, staring into its glazed eyes. Uncle Dan peeled the overalls off Hershel's torso, prying the snake loose from Hershel's fingers. He killed it and threw it into the bushes. Hershel wretched, vomiting a gallon of river water onto the pig weed beside him. Then he sat with his head between his legs. That's when I caught my first glimpse of It. It lay white and relaxed in the black hair of Hershel's crotch, like a sprout that had grown far from the sun. As Hershel recovered, he pulled his overall top over his lap. I acted like I saw nothing.

Somewhere outside my window a mourning dove cooed its morning song. I took a deep breath, stood up from the loom, and walked to the window to stare into the flattened grassy spot of the garden. I heard your voice.

"You're late," you bellowed.

"I know, Daddy. Ken didn't realize it was two."

You'd just come in from trying to catch Ken, who sped off fast. "He doesn't even have the decency to walk you to the door."

I poured a glass of water from the pitcher in the refrigerator and tried to drink nonchalantly. You were between me and the stairway door, leaning on the table, both palms pressed flat. I put the glass in the sink and turned to go upstairs.

"What were you doing this late, Angela? The movies were over by 11:30. The cafe closes at midnight. Nothing's open."

"We were just talking, Daddy." My voice sounded weak.

"Where?"

"In the cafe parking lot. Other kids were there too."

You slammed a palm onto the table. "Angela, it doesn't look good for a young girl to be out this late. Boys get the idea they can take advantage of you."

"Ken would never."

"In a car in the dark anything can happen." You looked me in the eyes.

I smiled. "Don't worry, Daddy. Trust me." I kissed you lightly on the cheek. You patted me on the back. Then in relief I skipped up the stairs, taking care to keep my step light so as not to awaken Mama or Dorothy.

10

I spread my hand across the growing fabric of my weaving. Carnal knowledge. I have suffered from the denial of it. Can you understand that, Daddy? I began the rhythm of the shudder again, thinking of the long drive to California twenty years ago, and Nevada.

Nevada is unlike any state I've ever travelled. It is empty, with distant mountains, always, and miles and miles of flat, drained land. It is blue, like an underexposed photograph. As I drove I tried to imagine a tractor pulling a plow in the landscape, but I couldn't. It would be like scratching the paint of a new car with a key. I had lost my radio two states back. Now my thoughts echoed in my head, until I could not tell what was thought and what was said aloud.

I was low on gas. I pulled into a station in Elko. The pavement was hot when I stepped from the car. I could smell asphalt and gasoline. My rubber thong stuck to the pavement.

In those days I thought nothing could hurt me. I was accustomed to the protective circle you had drawn about me, by the soybeans cupping the south side of our house and the corn stretching overhead. I knew the smells and they were friendly. Corn pollen sweetening the night air. Loam plowed deep and freshly turned offering the most intimate scent of the earth herself.

But then I was not in Illinois. I was out of range of your dime.

I never did know his name. He was tall with lemon hair, and he wore tight faded blue jeans and a plaid cotton shirt. He leaned against the gas pump, sunning himself. A loaded backpack rested on his right side. He watched me. I stood beside my Volvo as the attendant washed my windshield. My eyes focused somewhere beyond the truck stop ahead. The pump clicked, the attendant took a swipe at the rear window, and said, "That'll be $3.45." I paid him with a five.

He made his move as the attendant went to get change. Stepping toward me, hoisting his pack to his right shoulder, he said, "Going west?"

"Yes," I said cautiously.

"Mind if I ride to Reno?"

Don't pick up hitchhikers. That is what you said. Except you did once, when we were riding to Springfield in the pickup. We pulled to the side of the road, and you rolled my window down halfway. "Where are you headed?" Your voice was booming and commanding.

"Mason City," the man said. He was wearing a heavy tweed coat and nondescript pants.

"We are going to Springfield. I'll give you a lift that far. Hop in the back." You kept my door locked.

I wouldn't have offered this man a ride, but when he insisted, I didn't say no. I said, "I'm pretty filled up," and he motioned to the front and said, "Oh, I can repack this and I'll sit on my feet." So he tucked the pillow on the box of dishes in the back and we were soon driving down I-80 to Reno.

I remember his tanned forearms, large and muscular, and his blue jeans legs coiled in his seat.

At noon we stopped in Winnemucca. It was even hotter, and we found a spot in the shade of a building to eat the hamburgers we bought on the edge of the town. He drank a beer.

"So where are you heading?" he asked me. He ate his sandwich in big bites. Salad dressing dripped from the bun.

"California," I replied.

"Alone?"

"Yes," I said. "I'm going to school in the fall."

"All the way from Illinois?" He said the s. It made the state rattle.

"All the way from Illinois." Silent s.

He bent closer as we talked. First his foot rested on my naked calf. Then his hand brushed my thigh as he reached for his beer. I did not pull back. I was mesmerized by the growing warmth of a sun cradled on my pelvis. I could not move my gaze from the intense Nevada sky of his eyes, nor did I want to. I let him take me by the hand, let him lead me down behind a boulder, let him slip the buttons of my blouse through their holes and release the clasp of my bra. His hands were rough on my skin, and I shivered as his tongue traced my earlobes, my collar bone, my nipples.

I resisted when he slipped his hands below my waist band, but then exploded with pleasure. When he unzipped his pants, I sat up on my elbows. "I don't want to have intercourse," I said.

"You don't want to have intercourse," he mocked. "Where did you learn to talk?"

"I don't want to do it," I said again. I thought this was all that was required. I want this, I don't want that.

His eyes burned red as he leaned down on me. "Baby, I'm going to teach you something," he breathed. I smelled stale beer. His penis jabbed my stomach. I pushed him away.

"So you like it rough," he hissed, pushing me back to the ground. Dry grass stabbed my back. "You don't treat men like this. You don't get us going and then turn us off..."

I struggled and then felt a searing burn as he thrust hard and fast into me. There was a growing dampness between my thighs. When he finally rolled to the side, his penis showed the watercolor wash of my blood.

I pulled my clothes about me quickly and ran to the car. He did not follow. I fumbled for my keys and gasped with relief as my car door opened. I tugged at the backpack leaning on the front passenger seat until it cleared the steering wheel and then I threw it onto the pavement. I turned the key in the ignition, listening to the grinding of the starter, and when the engine finally turned over, I drove off with a screech. I saw him in the rear view mirror bending over his pack as I turned onto the highway.

I did not stop driving until I passed Reno. When I checked into a motel late that night, the upholstery of my seat was wet and stained red. I showered, washing every crevice of my body with soap. I put on my flannel pajamas and curled into a fetal ball, lying awake in the blackness. I got up when the maid knocked at noon. Honey, it's check-out time. Okay, I must have overslept. I'll be out in a jiffy. A week later when my period started, I tried to forget. And, of course, I never told you.

"Angela, what ever got into your head?" you would have said. "How could you ever let a strange man in your car?"

"I tried not to, Daddy."

"You didn't try hard enough."

"But I couldn't say no. He was too insistent."

"Well, then, you asked for it."

I couldn't stand to hear you say that. I couldn't bear to see the disgust on your face, the disgust that I'd been spoiled, soiled, ruined. So I didn't tell you then, or anyone else, until now.

Planting

THREE

The yellow bellied bull snake is one of the most valuable snakes. For the annual worth of one such snake to agriculturalists is said to be about fifteen dollars. The estimate is based on the fact that during its active season it consumes numbers of such crop destroying rodents as mice, rats, pocket gophers, and ground squirrels.

Will Barker, *Familiar Snakes and Amphibians of America*

1

"Mom, he's gone!" Wheat stood in the door of my studio.

"I know," I said, remembering his long, bronzed body slipping from the tent. "But I think he left a note. Look under the kitchen door."

He dashed to the kitchen and returned with a piece of lined paper. "It's in French," he said.

I took it. "'*Merci beaucoup, mes amis.*' Thank you very much, my friends," I translated. "'You were so kind for your hospitality. Tell your mother I was not disturbed by serpents. May our paths cross again. Jean-Pierre.'" I handed the note back to Wheat.

Wheat sank into the beanbag chair. His pajama legs pulled up to mid calf. He was outgrowing everything. "Couldn't he wait and say goodbye in person?"

"He probably didn't want to get caught up in storytelling," I said.

"No excuse," Wheat pouted. He was quiet. Then he said, "I wonder what he meant, he wasn't disturbed by serpents. Does he mean he didn't see any or that he wasn't upset when he did?"

"Good question," I said.

"Maybe he saw Vera."

"I doubt it," I replied. "Night is not the best time to see Vera."

"But if he saw a serpent and wasn't disturbed, it was probably Vera. And I don't think he'd be disturbed if he saw a serpent. So I think he saw Vera. She might have been in that high grass he pitched his tent in." He settled back looking pleased.

I said nothing. I just kept weaving. High grass triggered a memory of you, and baling hay, and of a summer when I was about Wheat's age. Each day during baling Mama, Dorothy, and I walked to the barns carrying a gallon mayonnaise jar of lemonade. After stashing the jar in a cool place, Mama would talk a minute or so to you and then leave us. "Now you watch your little sister and stay out of the way of the men," she'd commission me.

"Okay, Mama, we'll be fine, bye!" we said, already halfway up the ladder to the hay mow.

Not that she needed to tell us to stay out of the way. We wouldn't think of walking in front of the burly mass of Uncle Dan as he grabbed bales from the loader with gloves and grunts and heaved them to the side. We sat far enough away where we could watch Uncle Dan, and then Jimmy, and our cousins, Charley and David, both around Jimmy's age, who took turns stacking the bales on the ever-growing alfalfa mountain behind them. Besides, there were snakes, or pieces of snakes, dangling from the bales. "Here's one!" Uncle Dan called, and then we felt the energy rise about us. They killed the live snakes and threw them to the side, but left the dead ones, along with the snakes buried deep in the bales, to be discovered next winter, withered and dry, and to be eaten along with the hay by the sheep and cows.

I remembered one particularly hot day. By ten o'clock the horizon swam in heat waves above corn still reaching for its full height. Mama decided we should take the clinking, sweaty jar down early, and Dorothy and I begged to stay. "But it's so hot," Mama said. "Not to us," we argued. "We like it hot." "Okay," she conceded, "Okay, if you pick some lettuce for dinner first. I'll have my hands full otherwise."

"Hello, Morning Stars!" Uncle Dan called from the opening where the hay loader entered the mow. Then he turned to you as you were hoisting bales from the hay wagon to the loader. "'Bout time for a break?" You responded by turning off the motor. The intense grinding and squeaking stopped. We were left in an echoing silence. "Let's go, kids!" I heard Uncle Dan say, and before he finished his sentence, Jimmy, Charley, and David slid down the ladder. Uncle Will, who was helping you unload the wagon, slumped against the black walnut tree behind us. "Helloooo, girls!" he said, raising the jar of lemonade to his lips. His face, like the others', was covered with a thin layer of dust. He drank with a loud gulp and then passed the jar to you, wiping his mouth with the back of his hand.

The boys looked a generation older when working with you men, although, unlike you adults, they pulled off their tee shirts to expose their muscles. But they bore the same dust and sweat-grimed faces of you fathers and the implicit urgency to get the work done. It bent Jimmy early, that work. It set a rhythm in the youthful muscles of his back. He learned to work hard to beat the next thunderstorm or early snows.

This day the boys got a swig of lemonade and disappeared back into the barn. "Darn kids," Uncle Will said. "Hot as hell in there, and they're back in there first chance." After a respectful time, Dorothy and I poked each other and followed. "Darn kids," we heard Uncle Will say again.

The boys were sitting in the hallway of the milking stall on bales of straw, pieces of the yellow reeds protruding from their mouths like cigarettes. There was that new boy-man laugh, medium range except when it surprised us with a squeak. They were expecting us.

"Hellooooooooo, Morning Stars!" David croaked. Charley and Jimmy snickered. David was a smart aleck, always getting into it for his mouth.

"Shut up, Daaavid!" I said. He hit me in the leg with a handful of dirty straw. Dorothy grabbed his hair from behind.

"Hey, get this creep face off me," David yelled. He grabbed Dorothy's hand. Dorothy pulled harder.

"Dorothy, knock it off," Jimmy said, calm and adult-like. Dorothy stuck her tongue out but released her hold. Then she dropped on the bale next to me. "Besides," said Jimmy, "you interrupted us." And all three boys laughed wickedly.

"Well, don't let us stop you," I said testily.

"We won't," Jimmy answered. "It's time you learned the facts of life anyway." The laughter again.

"What facts of life?" I returned, keeping an edge in my voice.

"The only facts there is," Charley chimed in. "Like, your mom and dad Do It."

"Oh no they doo-oon't," Dorothy taunted, lips pulled back over large front teeth.

"Yes they do-oo," David mocked. "How do you think they got you?"

I wrinkled my nose and groaned.

"I read it," Charley said, "In Auntie's medical books." Charley had just spent the weekend with our Great Aunt Ida, who had gone to medical school a year. "There was even a picture," he added.

I almost believed him, but the picture was too much. "You're lying," I said.

"No, really!" David said in earnest. Evidently, he spent the weekend too. Then he looked at Charley and Jimmy and exploded into a hideous laugh. "There was this close up of the bun and wiener, cut in half, and the wiener was Doing It in the bun." The three boys laughed so hard this time they fell onto the ground. Jimmy threw straw at David, and then we were all throwing straw. "Come on kids, back to work," came the predictable stern voice of Uncle Dan. And quick as it started, it was over, leaving clouds of dust suspended midair as we climbed the ladder into the mow.

2

I learned just about everything I know about sex, until Nevada, in that barn. It was in the barn where we hid behind the bales, far from the adult world, with only the harvest of hay and snakes, and learned the excitement of viewing, though never, never touching.

Once when Jimmy had a friend Steve over to play, we ended a game of hide and seek in the haymow. Steve peed in a saucer I kept there to feed the cats milk drippings. I stood and watched the tender piece of flesh with the mauve tip and soft wrinkly bag at its base. As I stood staring, Steve stepped on the saucer, catapulting pee into my face, over my sweater, into my eyes. I screamed. Steve ran. But Jimmy stayed and dabbed the stinging liquid from my eyes with his sleeve, then led me down the ladder and out of the barn to the horse tank. He splashed my neck and face with the cold, thick water. Steve got brave again when he saw I wasn't going to tell and snickered. Jimmy finished brushing my sweater with his damp hands, and then he and Steve were off, running.

Jimmy was like that. He was one of them, but he was also gallant. We were not close, like Dorothy and me. We did not creep into bed together in the middle of the night when we were scared. We did not know the intricacies of each other's souls. But Jimmy was my brother, appearing in my darkest hours to protect me. I could count on him for that.

Jimmy spurred me on to do things I would never do alone or with just Dorothy. Once we climbed high into the box elder in the back-yard until we could see where the land reaches Osburnville and Macon, until we could see the grey towers of the grain elevators of Mt. Auburn. Jimmy was above me with his sure instructions. "Come on, Angela, now this branch, now that." I was scared, but I didn't stop. Not when I was with Jimmy.

Jimmy told me of the fat, black snakes living in the cribs, guarding the corn. "They eat rats," he said. I remember a rat running up Uncle Dan's pant leg when you were shelling corn. He yanked one pant leg off and then jumped up and down on that leg while trying to stomp the other pant leg off. His undershorts were surprisingly white.

We kids would run through the cribs like wild horses high on fresh air and land so flat it could be the sea. We ran by the snake's cribs and, when the corn was almost gone, we might find him coiled in the remains of last year's harvest. Jimmy would move quickly if he saw him, grabbing the snake behind his head before he could race through the boards, and now, I realize, as I weave, the weft of memory, the warp, imagination, into something darker.

"Hey!" Jimmy would yell, "I got 'im! Charles, Angela! Come quick..." and he would drape the heavy body from hand to hand, and, if the snake relaxed, let it crawl over his shoulder, like a boa. "Hold your hand out, Angela, he's very cool and smooth." Once or twice I did, standing there in the cribs in the days before I was an adolescent.

You fathers named him King Snake, and in the absence of your wives, allowed him to patrol the corn until next year when we would find him bigger still.

Most times we did not see or touch him. We entered the cribs, spurred on, perhaps, by the still boredom of summer heat. Leaning into our pull, we'd open the crib's large sliding doors enough to tuck ourselves into the cavernous interior. The smell of grease would meet us. When the forms of machinery you stored there emerged from our sun blindness, we went to a large rectangular storage bin either side of the center.

You warned us not to climb into the pool of shelled corn, but it wasn't because of snakes. You will sink and suffocate, you said. I wonder how many children didn't listen and jumped into the mounds anyway? In ecstasy they would sink into the cool corn kernels until every inch of skin was covered by the smooth and pointy surfaces. Who would find the children first, the fathers, or the Snake?

We only stared into our fathers' corn. And sometimes, as the corn lay below the dust of the crib, we could smell the Snake.

Jimmy noticed the musky smell first. It took practice to notice it, but once I did, I could never forget. At first it is just a distinctive other smell, not the tractor's dust-soaked grease nor the air thick with earth. It is not the sweetness of the corn. It is something much lower than all this: something that smells round, that tingles beyond our imagination. Perhaps it is the smell of the world moving through a gigantic birth canal, or, again, of the scream that carries us beyond the grip of orgasm, and into it, one way and the other, writhing back and forth, convulsing... But as children, we only smelled the musk. Then Jimmy would say, "Last one out is a dirty rat..."

3

Just after lunch there was a knock at the door. Mama was walking Kristen on the road. I had cleaned up the lunch dishes and was resting in the rocker in the living room. The house hummed with silence until the Bam! Bam! Bam! jarred me from my reverie. Willie jumped to his feet barking.

Jean-Pierre stood in the open doorway. "*Bonjour*, Angela," his voice sang when he saw me. "I have lost my tent stakes. I hope you do not mind if I search your garden."

"Of course not, go ahead." I sucked in my breath quickly as I stepped closer to the willowy man standing on the threshold of my kitchen. He smiled, his eyes meeting mine without hesitation. Green. I did not know his eyes were green. I thought they were brown, or grey, or something murky. I glanced away, flustered.

He laughed. "I did not tell you how beautiful are your weavings. They vibrate with color. They too are storytellers—is that not so, Angela?" He placed a hand high onto the door jam and leaned into it. A faint smell of perspiration drifted toward me, which was strangely appealing.

"They tell many stories," I smiled, shifting my weight from one foot to another. "So many stories that there's no more room for them on the walls or the floors really."

"Time for a larger space." His eyes met mine again. "Don't wait too long. Life is very short."

He reached for my arm and gave it a warm squeeze. I can still feel the imprint. He stepped back. "I'll go look for the stakes." Then he turned and descended the garden path, leaving me to contemplate: wait too long for *what*?

I remembered watching him dress in the garden that morning and the defined lines of the muscles of his back and buttocks. Perhaps I will follow him to the garden, I thought. Perhaps he'll pull me to him, enwrap me in his arms. The sun will warm us. I felt a warmth grow from deep in my pelvis. I watched the mosaic of madrone leaves against the sky. Then he was ascending the path, waving to me. "I found the stakes," he said, laughing. "*Merci beaucoup*. Until next time." I smiled, sad and relieved there wouldn't be a next time.

4

There is so much I forget. My life continues and I adapt. I have babies and Jake makes money to raise the babies. I cook and the babies grow requiring not less but different care: monitoring of homework, rides to baseball games, teacher conferences. I live my life like Marcy taught me to weave, trying to hold the whole in my heart, yet, have I forgotten what I was made of when it all began? I barely remember the fire that flared in the back seats of old Chevys, the passion of dusty barns in July, the urge to seek out the Other, the differentness, to explore beyond what I know. And then he arrives, he who tells stories and has no home. And his comment, don't wait too long, life is short? Should he not listen to himself? He has no children except those he weaves his stories for.

But the muscles of his back made my body remember the yearning I felt when I first met Jake.

All afternoon I thought of the storyteller and of Jake. I began to imagine his return that evening. I would wrap my arms about his waist, pull myself into his chest, sink my nose into the soft skin below his ear. Perhaps I would bite him gently, holding the skin lightly between my teeth. He would rub my back with increasing passion. We would fall into bed, hungry for the Other's touch, the Other's smell.

Jake called at 5:00 and said he'd be late. He had to meet with a student. I held the receiver composing myself as my mother sat at the counter beside me, alerted by my silence. "Okay," I said. I tried not to let the disappointment show in my voice. "When can we expect you?"

"Around nine. Tell the boys I'll be back before they go to bed."

"Okay. See you then." I hung up the phone without meeting Mama's eyes.

Later we hugged in the privacy of our bedroom. I sniffed his neck. He gave me a kiss on the forehead and pulled back. "I'm beat," he said. "I need to go right to sleep."

"Okay." My hand rested on his arm a second before I turned away. I dreamed of the ocean and the first time we met and once in the night I awoke, the waves of an orgasm moving up my pelvis. Or did I only dream that too?

5

Why I chose marine biology as a major I'll never know. I think I was out of my mind. I know you thought so, and Jake did too. Jake also said it was good for me, being out of my mind, and that it was probably the only reason I developed enough skill to live somewhere other than Illinois.

"Biology of the Marine-Land Interface. Influence of physical factors on adaptations of shoreline organisms." That is the catalogue description of my first course. And interface it was, too. An interface of what was known and what was not, of that which dissolves and that which works to stay solid and hard. Terra firma.

The first time I saw Jake was in class. He was talking to Dr. Witzweier, Professor of Marine Biology, leaning his whole body against the slate-covered lab table at the front of the room. When he looked toward the class and realized students were seated, expectantly waiting, he waved goodbye to Dr. Witzweier and left.

"*Guten Morgen, Meine Damen und Herren!*" Dr. Witzweier greeted us. As was his custom, he spoke in German and in English. "Welcome!" I wonder what you would have thought of him. He was a tall man with tawny hair and a reddish-grey beard, and had a habit of continually testing the humidity of the room during his lectures with a psychrometer, a small instrument he whirled about his head on the end of a strong cord. He recorded the readings on a corner of the blackboard and then washed the remaining boards down with water. The process continued throughout the hour.

The days he was not testing the humidity, he distilled ethanol which he collected in a beaker at the end of a long delicate glass apparatus. When he finished, he often sipped some of the ethanol, "Humm! *Lasst sich schon trinken!*" and then he poured the remainder back into the original beaker with the water and started over again.

This day, he was clearing piles of books from the front of a large salt water aquarium on the lab table. "Today we'll begin by discussing some inhabitants of the middle to low intertidal zones," he said in his gravelly voice. He peered around the front of the aquarium and pointed to a mass of purple spines on the bottom. "We have here a very fine fellow," he continued. "Research biologists think he is so fine for embryological experimentation that the sea urchin is in danger of disappearing totally from some areas." Dr. Witzweier was already resting the psychrometer in his palm, gently stroking the cord with his other hand. "*Strongylocentrotus purpuratus*! " he purred as he hurled the psychrometer into the air. The instrument orbited about his head. Everyone sat, transfixed.

"This fellow has adapted by digging protective holes into rocks in the middle-to-low intertidal zones of the open seas," he said. "This is how he manages the wave shock and the threat from the sunflower star.

"Sometimes he will move into the hole of an ancestor and grow larger than the opening. There he will be imprisoned for life. *Die Lehre hier ist: weilt nur nicht zu lange in den Hausen der Vorfahren.* The lesson here is this: do not linger too long in the homes of the ancestors." He cleared his throat. "He must live through a balance of being rooted enough not to be washed away, but mobile and autonomous enough not to be trapped."

He continued lecturing as he took a reading off the psychrometer, and marked the board. 72 , 58 . Then he drew a sea urchin's mouth.

"The sea urchin is actually a spherical starfish," he continued, "with three pedicellariae instead of two." He was washing the board again. The water dripped from the rag to the floor, but he didn't seem to notice. "I'll take you home today," he said to the purple spines in the tank, and then looking back at us, he continued. "This fellow can survive the beating of the waves against the shore, but not the calmness of the aquarium. *Die Stille lockt uns an. Aber Vorsicht! Sie kann auch lebensgefährlich sein.* Remember, calmness often beckons to us. But be careful; it can be fatal!"

Dr. Witzweier was known to spend hours at the coast, particularly during minus tides. He often invited students to accompany him. I learned through these trips the best time to walk the long, flat stretches of Salmon Creek beach and places to find the delicate disks of sand dollars. I learned to watch the tides and the inevitable sleeper waves, and to respect the tough and fragile life that richly populates the seam of the northern California coast.

Dr. Witzweier was preparing to launch the psychrometer again. "Miss Galway," he said as he swung the instrument into the air. "Mr. Murdock." He always called us by our last names. "Perhaps you would like to come with me this afternoon to escort Mr. *Strongylocentrotus purpuratus* to his ocean home."

We both quickly agreed. I forgot what else I had scheduled for the afternoon. Was it oceanographic chemistry? It didn't matter. It was an honor to be asked and no one refused. A student was said to have missed his 4:00 p.m. calculus final once because Dr. Witzweier invited him to take advantage of a December minus tide that occured at 4:14 p.m.

I had heard rumors about Dr. Witzweier's driving. Some students said it was the ethanol; others said he was too absorbed in talk to watch the winding roads and lane lines. So that afternoon I was relieved to see that Jake was driving. Dr. Witzweier sat in the front passenger seat of the VW van and Harry Murdock and I sat in the back. Several buckets, some filled with seaweeds, one with Mr. *Strongylocentrotus purpuratus*, sat between us and the front.

The drive turned out to be far longer and more trying than I imagined. The last third of the way I felt waves of nausea as Jake turned the steering wheel to the right and then the left, again and again. I watched the water slosh in the bottom of the buckets at our feet, and I was sloshing with Mr. *Strongylocentrotus purpuratus*, except he was probably at home in this wave shock and I was not.

On and on droned Jake's even timbre and then Dr. Witzweier's deep rumble, back and forth. Harry and I had long since fallen into silence.

At last there was the rolling of the VW camper door. I must have fallen asleep. The cool salt air hit me like the slap of a breaker hitting the shore, and I felt revitalized. We each grabbed two or three buckets as Jake locked the camper. Then we began the descent to the beach, Dr. Witzweier agile and sure of himself even in his rubber boots. He wore a worn brown leather aviator jacket and a heavy looking knapsack. A straw hat shaded his face into a checkerboard pattern. Jake followed in his uniform of patched blue jeans, fatigue shirt, and hiking boots. He also carried a knapsack. Harry was close behind Jake. I was not used to hills and my tennis shoes were slick. I sat on my heels and slid. When the trail evened out enough to stand upright, I walked. I hoped my feet would not slip and send me skidding through Harry, Jake and Dr. Witzweier.

It was the kind of day on the coast that, as I have come to know, happens only in September. The ocean reflected a deeper blue of the sky. A hazy mist separated the two at the horizon, and even the shoreline was uninterrupted by white water. It must have been on such a day that Balboa named it the Pacific.

By the time I got there, Dr. Witzweier and Jake were settling into a spot on the beach. "We have about 45 minutes until the tide is minus 1.5," Dr. Witzweier said. "Let's start over here and return these fellows to their pools as soon as possible." He pointed at the bucket beside me. "Mr. Murdock, would you grab that bucket?" Jake had already picked up a couple of smaller plastic buckets and a crow bar. "Miss Galway, would you bring the lenses?"

I stuffed a couple of folding hand lenses in my pocket and then grabbed one of the plastic buckets. Dr. Witzweier carried two buckets of starfish and started in the direction he had pointed. We followed, Harry behind Dr. Witzweier. Jake hung back with me.

My legs felt like they had become lead. "I never realized it was so hard walking in sand," I said to Jake.

"Where're you from, anyway," he said, smiling.

"Flat Rock. ...Illinois," I said.

"Flat Rock?"

"We lived near some bluffs on the river. One was especially tall and flat on top."

"Oh," he said, smiling again. "Never heard of it."

"Where are you from?" I countered.

"Cleveland, Texas,"

"How long have you been here?"

"Two years," he said. "I came for the marine biology program to study with Dr. Witzweier. He's one of the most outstanding marine biologists in the country." His eyes looked ahead affectionately. Then he looked back to me. "What ever brought someone from landlocked Illinois to California to study marine biology?" he asked, his eyes crinkling at the edges. He couldn't have been more than three years older than I, but there was a permanent crease on his forehead.

"Well, I always wanted to see the ocean," I said half seriously. Except it was true.

He studied my eyes a second. "You mean you had never seen an ocean when you decided to major in marine biology?"

"Until a month ago last Friday," I said, "I had never seen a body of water you couldn't see across."

"Jesus!" he said.

We reached the rocky shoreline. Dr. Witzweier was twenty feet out by now, balancing on a boulder here, a rocky ledge there, checking wildlife in each tide pool. Harry was several feet behind him.

"Mr. Murdock," Dr. Witzweier called. "Over here!" Harry hurried as fast as he could manage over the rocks slippery with lichens and moss, rough with barnacles, limpets, and mussels. Twice he slipped into the icy water. His pant legs were wet to his knees.

"Be careful, Angela," Jake warned as I started into the tide pool area. "It's easy to slip."

I slipped three or four times anyway. The water was freezing. How can an ocean so beautiful be so treacherous? Beach signs were posted, "Warning! Sleeper Waves!" with diagrams of undertows. At times, the signs stated, you are in danger on the beach twenty feet from the shoreline. Within months, I'd discover you could be in danger from twenty feet above, too. In fact, several life-changing experiences would involve immersion in this frothing sea. But those stories are to come.

Dr. Witzweier seemed oblivious to our problems negotiating the tide pools. He treated us as colleagues, as if we were already competent tide pool researchers. So we did not speak of the hardships to him, the scratched knuckles and knees, the numb feet and legs, the fatigue of constant vigilance. Instead we focused on the number of starfish on a particular rock or the speed of limpets moving away from a starfish.

I could see Dr. Witzweier gently returning the sea urchin to his home under a large boulder where waves rippled the surface even at this minus tide. He squatted surely on a rock and bent low as he released the purple ball of spines. As he turned, he called to Jake. "Mr. Tyler! This is our lucky day! Help Miss Galway over here, we have Mr. *Pycnopodia helianthoides!*"

Jake paused a second. "He's found a sunflower star, the largest known starfish. We don't see them often, so it's a treat when we do. Do you need help?"

"I'm okay," I said. "I'm getting my bearings." My feet were freezing by now. I was glad the sun was warm. Dr. Witzweier was still squatted at the tide pool fifteen feet ahead. Harry had slipped into a pool himself.

I slowly made my way over the rough and slippery rocks. As the textbook promised, the tide pools were full of life. Delicate lavender tentacles of anemones opened like flowers in full bloom. A hermit crab scurried under a rock displacing a many-legged animal which scurried under another rock. I moved like a giant through their domain.

When I reached Dr. Witzweier, he was gently turning over the iridescent orange sunflower star. "This fellow would rather lose an arm or two than be captured or trapped," he said, "so I must handle him with the utmost care. Many rocky tidal pool animals are like that, and it is necessary. If crushed by a rock they cannot possibly lift, they just leave the arm and grow another. Here, Mr. Murdock and Miss Galway, look at these feet."

The underside was covered by hundreds of yellow tube-like feet. The sunflower star lay quiet then slowly began to right itself.

"Mr. *Pycnopodia helianthoides* is hungry," Dr. Witzweier said. "He is hungry for Mr. *Strongylocentus purpuratus*. He is the sea urchin's second worst enemy, the first being research biologists."

As we watched, the sunflower star wrapped itself about a purple sea urchin. "He will eat what he needs and leave the rest," Dr. Witzweier said. My knees began to ache from squatting on the edge of the pool for what seemed like hours. I was relieved to stand when Dr. Witzweier asked me for the lenses. "Let's have a look at this algae here, Miss Galway."

The afternoon continued, the water in the tide pools becoming increasingly responsive to the swells lapping over the eroded rocks. "Time to get back," Dr. Witzweier said. He took a small notebook from his hip pocket and made a few notes as to the location of each animal he had collected that day. Harry and I leaned against a boulder. What appeared to be a rocky surface was, in fact, soft. I felt the inevitable squish of sea water soak the seat of my pants, but I was so damp by now it didn't matter. I had sat on a colony of small anemones.

I didn't notice the sleeper wave. Suddenly, Dr. Witzweier was yelling, "Drop! Quick, everybody! We are going to get wet! Hold onto the rocks for all you are worth! You are a limpet!"

As I fell, I felt the rude wash of icy water over my head, over my back. I scratched my arm but I didn't notice until much later on the beach. I was there, in the tide pools, with Mr. *Strongylocentus purpuratus* and Mr. *Pycnododia helianthoide*, with the limpets and chitons, the barnacles and mussels, all seemingly part of the rocks, and my hair was swaying in the current like tentacles, searching here and there for the loose crab, the unwary mollusk.

"Are you alright, Miss Galway?" Dr. Witzweier stood beside me, helping me to my feet.

How could I tell? I was too cold to feel anything at all. "I think so," I managed. I could see Jake a few yards away, also dripping wet. Harry had fared better, he had been far enough in to miss the wave. Dr. Witzweier was as wet as Jake and I.

"Waves are sneaky," Dr. Witzweier said. "This happens. Never run if you think you are about to be overcome. Don't think you can evade the fierceness of the ocean. Succumb to it, and cling, like these creatures, and you'll survive." He picked up a couple of buckets, now spilled of their contents, and started toward shore. Although he was at least thirty years my senior, he had unbounded energy.

Harry and Dr. Witzweier were on dry sand when I finally made my way back. Jake stayed a few steps behind me. I was shaking as we reached the log with the packs and he put an arm around me. "Poor Angela," he said. "And she hasn't even gone on the big trip yet!"

"What big trip?" I asked.

"The one to the Humboldt coastal wilderness next month. We go for ten days."

"Ten days!" I said. "What about the rest of our classes?"

"The other professors make provisions," Jake said. "We are looser here in California."

Dr. Witzweier was half way up the trail to the parking lot with Harry close behind. I picked up a couple of pails of hermit crabs and starfish. The sun was getting low and the air chilly. My damp clothes stung my skin. My lips were salty. The cliffs were golden, warm, and welcome.

6

When I remember my beginning into what was to become my brief, but eventful, sojourn into marine biology, I am again reminded of Trent's favorite story of the sea serpent Kolowissi. With what naivete we begin our big adventures; what a high price is exacted for transgressions! I wonder now, Dad, could it have been different? I still do not know the answer. But that fall semester, I began a process with more consequences than either you or I could have imagined.

Again, it was with Marcy that I first considered the meaning of my leaving you. She always thought the sea had called me to California. She called it *fate* and suggested I was baptized in that tidal pool, an emersion into new life. I remember this conversation well, because it confused me. We were sitting on her back steps in the heat of the sun the Russians call *grandmother's summer*, warm and waning. It was October.

"What do you mean," I asked, scandalized. Baptism is something my Christian religion reserved as a sacrament.

"The sea totally immersed you."

I watched her with reservation. Her thick black hair was loose and curled about her slightly plump face. "I came from a farm, Marcy, I am rooted in the earth, not the sea."

"Exactly. When things get too extreme, they right themselves."

"Oh." I was unaware that anything needed to be righted.

"Maybe you were returned to the primal waters," she continued, "It is where it all exists together, the acceptable and the unacceptable."

She was speaking another language as far as I was concerned. She continued talking about resisting, about fear of change. All I could think of was Dr. Witzweier's cry, "Hold onto the rocks for all you are worth!"

But now I wonder, was it baptism? Or did I go into suspension? There is a difference.

7

Within a couple of weeks of this conversation with Marcy, my class left for its ten-day field trip, arriving on an isolated, desolate beach by late morning. My grandfathers must have considered the prairie as uninhabitable as I considered the Humboldt coast that day. Dr. Witzweier was, of course, in his element. He hopped from his van, walked to the edge of the parking lot, and looked out upon the mist and the fog-laden beach that merged somewhere into an ocean. "Ah, beautiful!" he said, stretching both arms overhead. "Let's go meet the elements!"

There was grumbling about the fog, which was slowly becoming a light rain. I didn't want to leave the van. Sixteen of us began pulling on ponchos and unloading backpacks. "We've got an eight mile walk in to the base camp," Dr. Witzweier told us. "Ready, Ladies and Gentlemen? Let us begin our journey!" I would not see him again until evening when I limped into the base camp, exhausted and spent. He had already pitched his tent and had a fire going.

As I remember all of this, I'm glad I do not have to walk that beach now. It was long and tedious, with miles of soft sand and always the ebb and flow of water, up and back, loud and soft, like the rhythmic breathing of a giant. The day did not clear up. Instead it got darker, the sky laden with bluish-grey clouds that pressed closer to the earth with every step I took. At first we talked to one another, complaining about the sand, pointing out a sandpiper running in the surf, exclaiming as a golden elephant seal heaved onto a rock off shore.

We stopped occasionally for a snack, although the exertion obliterated my appetite. Jake held back the first miles, encouraging us to drink a sip of water often, naming a clump of bunch grass, shepherding us on. The sky gave no clue to the time. Jake eventually faded off ahead, along with almost all of the others. Two of us laggers tugged along, now quiet, not wanting to hear each other's thoughts. There was the incessant explosion of waves on the shore and then the inevitable tongue of foam reaching as far onto the beach as the power of the wave would permit.

"Breaking waves release tremendous amounts of energy on the shoreline," Dr. Witzweier said in a lecture earlier that week. "The shoreline forces the ocean's hand, and gets the impact of the energy of those waves and winds and sun stored in the wave. In time, the shoreline dissolves and is broken up. This is what it means to be on the seam," he added.

I thought of Marcy's suggestion that I had been baptized by the sea, but I didn't feel made new, I felt ground down, like the shore. "The ocean is a giant blender," Dr. Witzweir had said, "chopping off bits of shoreline all over our earth, whirring them together with the water and mud and debris from rivers. The result is a paradox: That which by its force brings such change to the face of the earth, in the very course of its action, minimizes the variation of salinity and temperature of its waters. This great blended medium we call "ocean," the product of millions of years of solvent action on rocks, soil, organisms, and the atmosphere, remains a fairly constant 96.5% pure water, water which itself is the medium for most chemical reactions which sustain life!" He had said this triumphantly, with a flush growing across his cheeks, which Harry claimed was due to the ethanol.

I remembered that lecture as I walked through sand that sucked my feet into the earth. Mist dampened my face and hands with beads of pure water covering my poncho with an infinity of warty-looking droplets. I'm becoming an amphibian, I thought. Or was the ocean dissolving and grinding me down too? Am I the wave formed on the open flats, rushing from my spawning ground to become unstable and crash into the Other? Am I that which grinds or that which is ground down, that which forms or that which is molded? I felt dizzy thinking about it.

By the time I saw the glow of campfires far ahead that first night, the sky contained its last grays and was about to give in to total blackness. My calves felt incapable of another step; my shoulders protested the weight of my pack so much I had to hold my pack's frame ends on the sides so the straps wouldn't touch my shoulders. Jake was sitting at a campfire with two other students as I walked up. "We're all here," he said jovially. "Quite a walk, huh?"

I dropped to a driftwood log and pushed the straps of my pack off my raw shoulders.

"You can use my fire," Jake said. "You'll feel better after you eat."

Although I didn't want to move, I forced myself to dig through my pack until I found a freeze dried dinner. I somehow managed to hydrate what seemed like desiccated remains and then to improvise a tarp lean-to against a beached tree trunk several feet from the fire. Even though the ocean was not tormenting with the crashing breakers of several hours ago, I could hear it lapping against a shore I could only guess was there. "I think I'll go to bed," I said to several sitting around the fire. "See you tomorrow. "

The rain picked up. Although my lean-to was holding up, I added a couple of large rocks to the top edge, then skimmed off my poncho and slipped under. Sand stuck to my hands and knees; I brushed it off as best I could before pulling off my jeans and sweatshirt and slipping into my bag. It felt deliciously familiar. I rolled my jeans into a ball and used them as a pillow.

I must have slept. Sometime in the night I was startled awake. "Ladies and Gentlemen! Quick! You are about to become wet! Your tents are below high tide line!" A cold tongue of water licked my ear as it dampened the upper edge of my sleeping bag and my jean pillow. I leaped up, the air and tarp cold against my bare back, and the tarp jerked away from the log. Cold water splashed onto my ground tarp. I yanked my sleeping bag up quickly.

An almost-full moon hung high over the ridge to the east. White clouds rushed between its lopsided roundness and me. I grabbed my pack and tucked the sleeping bag up so it wouldn't drag on the sand. Then I ran up the beach and dumped them several yards away. I returned for my jeans, flashlight, and tarps. Three other students were also hurriedly moving about. I could hear the low murmur of voices.

My jeans and ground tarp were soaked. I grabbed them and dragged them back to my pile. I was rummaging through my pack, trying to find my other pair of jeans, when I heard a still, soft, "Angela?"

Jake. Oh my god. I was standing there nearly naked in the light of the almost full moon. "Yes," I said. "Just a minute, excuse me, my jeans got wet. I'm looking for another pair."

"Oh," he said uncomfortably. I watched him out of the corner of my eye. I could tell he was considerately staring at the ocean. "Did you get real wet?" he asked after a few seconds.

"Only my jeans and the top edge of my bag," I said. I quickly pulled on dry pants. My legs were like sandpaper.

"I have plenty of room in my tent," Jake said. "Why don't you put your bag in there? Although it is clear, it could rain in ten minutes."

"Thank you," I said, not looking him in the eye. "I'm not in the mood to set up my tarps again tonight."

We caught each other stealing a glance at the other. A wave broke.

"Let's get some sleep then," Jake said.

Jake's tent was round and igloo shaped. Once in, he pulled his bag to the side and then stretched my bag out on the other. Then he turned out the flashlight, unzipped his jeans and pulled them off, skinned his sweat shirt off over his head, and crawled into his bag. I casually followed suit. The sleeping bag was warm against my bare legs but cool at the bottom. It was smooth against my breasts. I wondered a minute if I should have worn a tee shirt to bed, but I didn't want to go back to my pack to get it. There was silence. "Goodnight, Angela," Jake said softly. "Good night," I returned.

I listened to the waves, which eventually merged into Jake's heavy breathing. Soon I slept. When I opened my eyes, the tent glared white. Where am I? I quickly glanced towards Jake's bag. He was gone. I breathed a sigh of relief, sat up, dressed. I thought of you for a second, relieved you were not there. What would you have thought of me, having slept beside a man I barely knew?

The morning was brilliantly clear. Students bent over campfires here and there. No one else was up yet in our area, and Jake was not in sight.

I stretched my arms high, feeling the cool morning air hit my stomach. The ocean was quiet again. There was only a lapping as small white waves broke several feet offshore, then smoothed over the rocky tidal pool area to my right. I searched for a name for the color of the ocean. Azure? Turquoise? Serpentine green?

Something had happened in the night. I could hear it in the call of the sea gulls. I dug my toes deep into the sand. For the first time in my life, I felt something hot swell from within. When I sat very still watching the waves caress the rocky tidal pool area, I could feel it strong, like a sprout buried deep in the earth that is on its way up.

"Good morning, Miss Galway!" Dr. Witzweier said, coming up behind me. "Did you have a good rest?"

"Great," I said. "I feel wonderful."

"Did you get dried out?" he asked, sitting on the log opposite me. He was dressed in a white windbreaker and grey flannel pants.

"I didn't get that wet really," I said. "I'm okay."

"Where's your tent?" he asked looking about.

"Jake said he had room in his tent, so I slept there for last night." I was suddenly overwhelmed with guilt. If Dr. Witzweier noticed he didn't care.

"Good, then you were dry." He stood up, brushing the sand from the seat of his pants. "We'll meet over by the tide pools in an hour. See you then!"

Jake was returning as I walked to the stream to get more water. He was carrying a stringer with three trout. "Dinner," he smiled. "Want to join me?"

"Sure," I said.

8

It happened very quickly. Jake said later the ocean always does that. The old is dissolved, and then new possibilities open up. Things happen faster in solution. That afternoon Jake and I walked upstream to look for the patch of watercress he had seen earlier on his fishing trip. "Let's swim," Jake said, pulling off his clothes. I stood spellbound. His body was lean and forbidden, yet I looked at every muscle, the tautness of his belly, the bulging of his thighs. His chest was covered with the same chestnut hair of his head. He dived unselfconsciously into the pool. I watched the curve of his buttocks as he hung midair and then, ever so slowly, slipped into the deep waters. He came up sputtering. "It's wonderful, Angela, come on in!"

I paused a second. I have no swimsuit, I almost said. I unbuttoned my blouse. The sun hit my chest. I felt the air on my buttocks as I pulled my jeans from my feet. I felt the sprout again. It filled my pelvis. I stood nude, toes grasping granite, and pushed with all my might. Jake's eyes met mine. I felt them travel over my breasts, my stomach, my legs stretched behind me. I felt the water cold against my face, my shoulders, my thighs. In a baptism, I was immersed. And when I surfaced, there was Jake inches away from me laughing. "Angela," he said softly. I felt his hand on my waist, and I swam closer, hungry for the curve of his back. "Angela," he whispered, and I could smell him. Even in the water, he smelled like grassy fields, his breath was alfalfa.

I watched his teeth. They were white and even. His mouth opened slightly and I drew closer as if to hear a secret. His arms encircled me and I felt his chest against my breasts, his penis hard on my belly. Is that the sprout? I thought. Is that the sprout that grows within me and pushes up?

We didn't make love that afternoon. How we stopped ourselves is a wonder, but we didn't have condoms. "I'll borrow some," Jake said.

When we dressed and walked barefoot back along the path, I felt a strong invisible cord connecting us. Any distance, even a few inches, brought a tension, and I longed for release. By the time we reached camp, the sun was low and orange over the ocean. We built a fire for the trout and watched the sun melt into the sea.

Several other students joined us at the fire. I tended it like an altar, adding pieces of driftwood to make its blaze high and satisfying. Jake sat beside me, cleaning the fish. I could feel the hairs of his leg brush my calf. The evening chill made my skin rough, but I dared not cover up with a layer of clothing. I burned warm inside, and my skin's coolness was a pleasant contrast.

When I wasn't feeding the fire I watched Jake. Everything about him warmed me. His smile. His laugh. The way his knees jutted to the sides when he sat on the log bench. His windbreaker opened at his throat and chest. When we brushed each other, I felt the tension within me melt, like the sun sinking into the ocean.

The trout was delicious, but in that state, barnacles would have been delicious.

Do they know, I'd wonder. Has Jake asked Ken? Can they tell by the way I watch him, by the way our eyes lock? Do I put out a scent? Can they tell by my scent how much I yearn for him? Can they tell by my hunger? By the way I chew each bite, by the way my mouth waters when I see him?

That night I moved into Jake's tent for good. We unzipped both bags and used mine as a comforter and his as a ground cloth. Then we lay entwined to stay warm. I was mesmerized by his smell. His sleeping bag smelled like him. His shirts smelled like him. Even his backpack smelled like him. I breathed him deep; I tasted the saltiness of his neck and earlobes; I felt his muscular body insistent and strong against mine.

The tide rose. All evening and night, the frothing waters reached for us and Jake said, "We're all right, Angela, the tide is about the same tonight as last." So I let go and let the ocean's roar carry me through a slow-breathing rhythm. We slept a while and made love, slept a while and made love, awakening each time to a humidity that drew us closer and started it all over again. Once when Jake entered me, I felt a fissure deep within. I felt it, I heard it, and I clung to Jake, and like a chiton to a rock, I let the wave pass over. "Do not resist," Dr. Witzweier had said. "If the wave overtakes you, cling to the rocks." My hair swayed with the motion, I could feel it floating on the jean pillow. When it was calm again my face was in Jake's shoulder and I was intoxicated and tired. Again, I slept.

For seven days I lived with the ocean's rhythm, its crashing waves and periodic tides, setting my internal clock to the ebb and flow, collecting shellfish when the tide was out, going upstream when it was in to bathe in a clear pool or to hunt for herbs for dinner. I would peel off my clothes and walk barefooted over the rocky path. The air was often cool and stinging to bare flesh. I felt like the animal I was. By day I hunted and by night I survived the tides and made love.

Only once during the trip did I think of snakes, and that was when Jake caught a large king snake. "Angela," he called, "come touch its skin. It's smooth, cool." But I wouldn't, although I did stand close and I didn't scream. Not once did I think of a snake-in-the-sleeping-bag story that Jimmy used to tell. "Zip up your tent," he'd say. "Bill Barnes didn't. He woke up with a snake curled on his chest and he had to wait until the sun hit the bag for the snake to crawl away."

"Shut up, Jimmy," I'd say.

"Don't listen to me," he'd taunt. "Just wait and see. You'll be sorry."

But snakes didn't worry me in the Humboldt wilderness.

On the eighth day, there was a storm. We awoke to a sky dark and pregnant with rain. The winds rose, lashing our tents as they whipped the waves. We all rode the storm out in our tents. At first Jake and I watched the waves pounding the shore through a crack in the door, but we grew tired of that and spent the rest of the morning making love. At noon we walked through the wet, high winds to get water from the stream. On returning we ate dried fruit and nuts and biscuits left from our last evening's meal. Then we took a walk over the beach, which was as deserted as the moon. No one was out. "Let's drop in on Dr. Witzweier," Jake said.

Dr. Witzweier's tent was zipped tight. "Dr. Witzweier!" Jake called.

"Uh? Hallo!" the answer came, followed by a zip. As he stuck his head out. His eyes were red, his face flushed. "What are you two up to?"

"Visiting," Jake smiled.

"Uh, well, come on in. I'm just having a sip of brandy. Please join me."

The tent reeked of alcohol. It was an old four-man tent with the top sloping down either side to a two foot wall. On one side was his unrolled sleeping bag. On the other was his backpack and several field guides and notebooks. He motioned for us to sit down and passed the brandy to Jake. His hand was shaking. Rain pelted the tent with renewed vigor.

Jake took the bottle and drank a swig, then passed it to me. I did the same, almost choking. The liquor burned as it flowed into my stomach. Jake grinned. "Take it easy, Angela," he said. I glared back.

"This is quite a storm," Dr. Witzweier continued. "Quite a storm indeed." He lay on his sleeping bag. "Not often do we get to experience a storm this intimately. The pounding of the waves, the flapping of the tent as it defends one from the winds, the coldness. Not a day for a fire, no, so we have to rely on this." He reached for the bottle and drank a long drink.

Jake and I exchanged glances. Dr. Witzweier sunk back on his elbows and then collapsed on his back. His eyes were closed. "Well, I guess we'll be going," Jake said. "I'll check to make sure everyone is dry."

"Thank you, Mr. Tyler, thank you." Dr. Witzweier said, his eyes still closed. And then he was silent. We crawled back through the unzipped flap and I carefully zipped it back again.

We walked from tent to tent. Some students were playing cards, some reading. We helped Harry drive his tent stakes back into the sandy spot he'd chosen and covered the stakes with big rocks. When we returned to our tent, a couple of students were there. "Our tent ripped," one said. "Can we stay with you?" So they moved in.

The storm did not let up. The sand was wet and strewn with damp pieces of seaweed and driftwood. We watched enormous swells push toward the shore and break into great foaming white water. Late afternoon the rain subsided only long enough for us to build a small, smoldering fire to heat water for dehydrated noodles. Dr. Witzweier did not emerge from his tent that afternoon, nor all the next day. There were many snickerings about his being on a roll. As night came, and with it renewed winds and rain, we all withdrew into our tents again. Once in Jake's tent, the four of us played bridge until our fin-

gers were too cold. Then we turned out the flashlight and crawled into
our bags. Jake and I fell asleep immediately. Some time in the night
we awoke kissing and ever so slowly, we made love, trying to do it
soundlessly. I swelled like the ocean, crashed like the waves. I never
knew it could be like that.

Dr. Witzweier joined us that morning as we walked out, looking
tired and spent. He still managed to stay far ahead. I walked with
Jake, the wet sand harder beneath my feet and easier to maneuver on
than the trek in. The ocean was furious. Its white water leaped at the
heavens. "I'll miss the ocean," I said to Dr. Witzweier when I caught
up with him on the way out. "It has become a part of me these last
days."

"It had always been a part of you, Miss Galway," he said.

"You were just too landlocked to know," Jake grinned. He could
say almost anything to me with that grin, and he has.

But they were right. The sound of the ocean is the pulse of life.
Coming and going. Ebb and flow. Calm and violent. I began to see
how it is like the roaring silence of the midwinter prairie, or then
again, like the pulsating beat of my heart. Hush, listen.

We got back before dark and quietly loaded the vehicles. I sat in
the front seat with Jake, and he drove with a hand on my leg. It
poured all the way back to Santa Rosa.

9

December 17, 1970

Dear Angela,

   The crops have been in for several weeks now. Good thing, too.
We have several inches of snow this morning, and we had snow
last week and Thanksgiving week as well. Snow never did the crops
any good. As it is we don't have to worry about the weather much,

except whether the school bus can make it through. No trouble this morning, though. I had Will help me put the snow plow on the tractor, just in case. They are saying it's going to be a hard winter.

Jimmy was home several weekends during corn picking. He drove the truck to the elevator. We had to be a little careful. The state police parked off the road in Osburnville several days. Got Bill Rice. There's barely a truck in the county that could pass inspection. We averaged 180 bushels per acre. Not bad for a dry year.

Your mother got me to get that dishwasher she's been wanting. Jimmy helped me with it last time he was home. We also found a cider press at the auction last Friday. We are getting too many trees to just make applesauce, even with you and Dorothy helping.

I hope it will seem like home to you when you come back in June. There are changes, but only small changes. They shouldn't make a difference. We are the same family.

Love, Dad

10

December 17, 1970

Dear Dad,

This year is far more than I ever expected. Dr. Witzweier, my marine biology professor, is one of the top marine biologists in the nation, and not only does he know his material, but he's a great teacher.

He is a bit eccentric, but then I guess we are all to someone somewhere else in this world. Jake—remember I told you about the teaching assistant in my Interface course?—said Dr. Witzweier knows more than anyone and Jake came here just to study with him.

You would like Jake. He's a year older than Jimmy. His grandfather was a sheriff in east Texas.

If I want to take Marine Mammals, I have to wait until next fall. It is not offered spring semester. So I don't know. It depends on if I decide to stick with marine biology as a major. I have time to decide.

Love, Angela

P.S. We were at the beach yesterday in short sleeves. Can you imagine? Short sleeves in December?

Cultivating

FOUR

It is absolutely necessary to do the things that interest the god, one of the hardest things..., and it is just here that the snake is our best hope for it represents that instinct which knows what interests the gods and makes us do it...

Barbara Hannah, *Symbolism of Animals*

1

At 5:30 the next morning we got a call from Jimmy. He had forgotten the time difference and had been up for hours. His voice was short and businesslike, but this alone didn't surprise me. As you know, Jimmy is not a telephone talker. He states his business, and that is that.

"Is Mama there?" he said.

"Of course. Do you want me to get her?"

"Yes." A solitary yes. Metallic, in sharp contrast to the morning fog erasing the redwoods outside the living room windows. I went to get Mama, feeling annoyed.

"Jimmy's on the phone."

Her body, relaxed in sleep, suddenly jerked, contracted, a sea anemone touched in its intimate depths. In that movement she was on her feet.

The phone call was long by Jimmy's standards. Five minutes. I did not catch Mama's words. Her voice, though, was first questioning, then insistent, then slowly the insistence dispersed. Her words careened outwards like globes of mercury, shattered, and shattered again.

I was washing my face in the bathroom when she hung up. Without a word, she went back to bed.

2

"How's Jimmy?" I asked Mama at breakfast. She hadn't said a word about him since the call.

"He's got his hands full," she said. There was a long pause. Then, "He barely has time to do the field work. Jess Carter keeps him busy butchering. And those boys of his!"

Those boys of his. I know. They wear us all out. "I'll bet they're getting big," I said.

"Too big to be running around like hoodlums," she said. "He's going to have real problems when they are a year or so older and start driving. He ought to have them walk the beans or do some of the cultivating. But no. Michael's on the swim team and has to practice mornings and John rides his bike all over town but can't walk a quarter of a mile if he's in a bean row. Those boys don't have enough supervision and they are going to get in a lot of trouble! Laziness spoils boys."

We were quiet. Kristen slept in her swing, and Mama adjusted a pillow under her neck. "That little neck looks like it could break off," she said.

I'm sure you'd be the first to say it wasn't laziness that drove Jimmy off the farm. We all knew it was coming. Even at Jimmy's birth I think you knew. But we ignored it. He was raised like a prince who would inherit his father's kingdom. He had the room at the end of the hall, opposite Mama's and yours. Dorothy and I shared the room in between. Ours was a pretty yellow room with its rattling windows stretching within inches of the floor, but Jimmy's room was rambling. I thought of it more as a suite, with shelves of model airplanes and an electric train that was perennially set up to run through tunnels and over bridges. Dorothy and I could watch. Occasionally Jimmy let me work the levers that moved the train like a mad mouse over the miniature terrain. But usually it was you and Jimmy who worked there, mending track, tightening loose train wheels, perfecting paper maché furrows in a field.

But Jimmy couldn't earn a living farming. You can't divide a farm five ways, and then three again, and have enough land for a son to take over. For years we ignored that fact, because it wasn't fact yet. So when Jimmy left the farm to go to Cornell, it must have felt like a betrayal. When he wasn't there for harvest or for springtime plowing, you walked heavier, and stayed out in the field later, and were quieter at noon. Jimmy couldn't suffer it. Upon graduation, he was back, planting during the hurried season of spring, harvesting in the fall. Then one year you mortgaged the farm, using the money as a down for 200 more acres. Everyone was happy and hopeful. Life would continue. Jimmy was home.

When we were kids, we thought the farm would go on forever. We sat on the new horse tank, the one Grandpa built twenty years before, and watched three-inch goldfish dart in and out of the thick algae. We could smell the frothy sweat of work horses, although they'd been sold years ago, when Grandpa found no use for them except eating the cows' rations. So, although the cows had been the only users of this tank for years, it was still called a horse tank. Their harnesses still hung in the barn. Things linger a long time on the farm.

We were cradled in the illusion that life was constant. This was Grandpa's land, and his father's before him. We thought it had been in the family forever. We ignored the warning from the tiny pieces of flint carved into points that Grandpa and you found when you plowed. Three generations was eternal enough for us to not worry about much change in this lifetime.

Mama and I finished the dishes. The boys raced out the door to a new summer camp where Jake enrolled them. Trent, in an act of solidarity, had also refused to return to the first. I wanted to weave, but with Mama there, I felt uncomfortable slipping away to the studio that time of morning. I suggested a walk. I put Kristen in the baby carrier, the one that held her next to my chest, and we started down the road. Willie ran ahead fifty feet and waited, ran ahead and waited. I breathed deep to catch the pungent bay laurel, the redwood tang.

"Jimmy thinks we should put the land up for auction," Mama said. She's never been one to sneak up on something. You never think, okay, okay, get on with it.

The air got caught in my lungs. It didn't want to come out. No more wanted to go in. "What?" I asked weakly.

"Jimmy says we should auction the land," she said. "The bank is calling in the loan. We can't pay it. The seed company is demanding the money up front. We don't have it. The price of corn has dropped. It isn't working anymore. Jimmy says we should pay off the forty acres the house is on, he can farm it weekends, and auction the rest. He'll pick up more hours at Carter's."

Grandma Galway said she lived too long. She lived to see things she never wanted to see. She watched a grown son die, and she sat at the death bed of every sibling she had. She saw close friends succumb one by one to stroke, cancer, ailing hearts. "I can't stand to live this long," she told me. "I didn't plan to see all these people die."

I wish I had not lived to see this day. I envy you. You did not have to make the decision that sealed the fate of this family. No, Jimmy had to make it.

Mama had tears in her eyes, but they were frozen there. She did not see in or out. Some people think it is strange we do not talk at times like this. But there was nothing to be said. We walked home, silent. I think I'll weave, I said. The yarn felt soothing against my fingers. There was the familiar rhythm. Raise the shuttle, turn, reposition the yarn, put the tractor in low, and move slowly forward.

3

The last time I felt like this was when you died. Jimmy called then too, about noon. "Dad collapsed this morning," he said. "He came in early for lunch because he didn't feel good, and then just collapsed. He's in intensive care. We don't know much yet. I think you should come."

The moment had called for action. Call Lloyd and Irene, arrange for the boys to spend some days there, no we didn't know how long. Fly to St. Louis, checking in by pay phone every chance. "Are you family?" the voice on the other end would always ask. "Yes, I'm his daughter," I'd say. It became a mantra. I'm his daughter, I'm his daughter, I'm his daughter. "His vital signs are weakening. No, he is not in pain," the voice would report. "Come on, Angela," Jake'd say, "our plane leaves in ten minutes," or, "I got us a car, let's go," but I'd linger a second, as if I could give you life if I stayed on the line.

"Stop in Litchfield, stop in Raymond, stop in Taylorville," I'd say. Jake did, searching out the phone under a solitary street lamp or in the parking lot of a Shell station. The night was hot and damp and dark. It rained earlier and puddles filled pavement irregularities with pools of black water that shimmered rainbows in the street light. "Are you family?" I'm his daughter. Is this the last time I can say it, I'd wonder as I formed the words carefully with my tongue. Perhaps I could save them, keep them on my dresser with the crinoids you and I found in the gravel when I was seven.

Jake and I didn't talk and I didn't cry. It was too damp to cry. My throat swelled shut. I could not breathe. I rested my head on the seat back. "Stop in Boody," I said.

"It won't help," Jake said softly. "We'll get there sooner if..."

"Stop in Boody," I said.

We stopped at a small abandoned store front that I remember to have been a post office and filling station. There was a phone booth nearby. The nurse recognized my voice. "Let me call your brother," she said. "He's right here."

There was a pause, long and hollow, then the echoing voice of Jimmy. "Angela, he's gone. There was no pain..." and I heard only sobs, man sobs, that reminded me of adolescent boys' voices, high and low. Something broke loose in me too. I could feel its force in my chest, rushing toward my eyes, pushing sounds I must have been making into the phone booth. My knees weakened until they buckled and I slid down the side of the booth, gasping for air. Then Jake was hanging up the receiver, helping me stand. "He's gone!" I sobbed, and Jake held me. There was a light sprinkle. I could feel it on my arms. The air was heavy in my lungs. "He's gone."

4

We were quiet the two days after Jimmy's call about the land. When we did talk, it was with effort. Our eyes were at half mast, and we did not make eye contact. When Kristen fussed, I returned to feel milk flowing in my breasts. But when she drained that milk and fell asleep, the energy was also gone. When I carried her to her crib, she was heavy. I could feel the earth tugging her. When I laid her on the cool printed sheet, I felt lightened, and weak, like I had just delivered her and was suddenly twenty pounds lighter, alone with myself.

Mama sat in the rocking chair in the living room when I was not nursing Kristen there, and she rocked. She moved very slowly, sometimes with her eyes closed, sometimes open but glazed. "It was a year ago next week that your father died, Angela," she said once. "Yes," I said. The sound of a human voice was refreshing, but neither of us followed up, and we fell back into silence until Kristen fussed, or Wheat and Trent returned from camp, or Jake came home for dinner.

By the morning of the second day, I had no energy to weave. I don't remember how the day passed. There was no energy to remember. "What did you do today, Angela?" Jake asked, and I searched my memory for a glimpse of something.

"Not much," I said.

"Did you weave?" he asked.

"No, it is hard to weave with Mama here."

"It might help." There was a note of tenderness in his voice. I was grateful for the concern, but I said nothing. Jake did not understand what was happening to Mama and me. Our energy had sunk deep in the earth, and we moved so as to expend as little as possible, because it was so scarce.

The morning of the third day Mama emerged from her room with a forthrightness. "You look happier, Grandma," Wheat said at breakfast.

She looked at him in surprise, as if he were an intruder or trespasser, though not an unwelcome one. "Well, I guess I am," she said.

It was silent again. "You've been so quiet," Trent commented.

"I guess I have. I've had a lot of thinking to do."

"About what?" Wheat asked, taking a giant bite of toast.

"Oh, about the farm, about what we should do. That farm has been in our family for over a hundred years. It's hard to think of letting it go."

"Why are you going to let it go?" Wheat asked.

"It's just too expensive to farm."

"Won't it be too expensive for someone else too?" Wheat pressed.

"Hard to say. Depends. But if we put it up for auction, I'm sure there will be some bidders. Then it will be their business." She sipped her tea cradling the cup in both hands.

"Who owned it before our family?" Trent asked.

"A man named Jeffers, I believe. Great Grandpa Galway bought it from him."

"How long did Jeffers own it," I asked.

"I don't know, I'm not sure he even farmed it. Great Grandpa tiled it. Before that it was mostly swamp. Swamp and rattlesnakes." Mama took a bite of toast, and chewed it carefully. "The land wasn't settled much until the railroads went through. When those Russians left Fort Ross, most of Illinois was still virgin prairie."

"When did the railroads go through?" Trent asked, scraping yogurt out of his bowl.

"The 1850's," Mama answered. "Really not very long ago."

"Seems like a long time to me," Wheat said.

"It seems shorter the older you get." The resignation in my own voice surprised me.

"One hundred twenty years ago there were no cars, few railroads, and the West was still wild. Things have changed more in those 120 years than they have in any other 120 years in history." Jake was off and running.

"We know that, Dad." Trent's voice cracked as he said it.

Jake grinned. "Okay, wise guy, no more history lessons for you! Time for me to go anyway." He gave me a kiss and then bent to kiss Kristen.

"Watch out for the Leech," Wheat said. "She'll attach herself to anything warm."

Jake grabbed his shoulders from behind and Wheat twisted in mock pain. "I'll be back this afternoon," Jake said to me. "The faculty meeting was canceled." He patted Trent on the shoulder, "Behave with the rangers." He turned to Mama, "See you later, Eleanor," and he was out the door.

Moments later we heard a car honking. "There's your ride!" I said, and the boys were gone.

Mama and I returned to the quiet. Is it the silence of the prairies we have here, I wondered, a silence interrupted only by the hushing wind through big bluestem prairie grass? My ancestors came to tolerate silence. They had to in order to live in the sparsely populated flat lands. They came from Ireland and the east, Connecticut and Ohio, and they bought land from the government at the inflated price of $2 per acre, or from earlier discouraged buyers, like Jeffers, who were happy to unload their plots. They had no idea what was involved to get the rich black loam they found beneath the tangled roots of the grasses, beneath the marshes that flooded much of the land, to produce a livelihood. So they used their prime years burying tiles to drain the land and carving deep black furrows. They planted wheat, oats, and corn, and they weaned themselves from the sounds and activity of civilization. Silence was what endured before and after.

When I was a child, I would walk to the center of your fields and stand, listening. In the spring and summer, there was the sweet, melodic song of redwing black birds and the squawking of ring-necked pheasants. In the fall the world vibrated with crickets and grasshoppers. But in the winter, when the world was wrapped in a blanket of white, there was no sound at all, only earsplitting silence. If I moved my foot, the crunching would interrupt, make the silence settle down. But then, if I stood absolutely still again, the sound of that other world came back. Perhaps our everyday sounds just distract us, make us insensitive to silence. Perhaps that is why newborns scream. They leave the rumbling, thumping world of their mothers and for the first time hear the silence. My ancestors knew that silence. They had to endure it in order to coax the land to grow their crops. It rested outside their houses at night and met them in long, lonely winters when distances became dangerous. It sentenced them to few or no doctors and to a social life as sparse as the trees. Some thrived on it. It got in their blood. But others suffered the immensity of the prairies. They grieved the lands and people they left or the loss and hardships of what they met in arriving. Loneliness was a given, like the sun rising and setting, like the flatness of the always visible distant horizons, like the black loam that grew the corn, oats, and wheat. And, because it was a given, it was not discussed.

My mother and I have the silence of the prairie in our blood. We find comfort in grieving the way of my grandmothers and great-grandmothers. At such times we speak only of the ordinary, the immediate, our attention on the work at hand. On the morning of the third day we worked. We cleared the kitchen table and loaded the dish washer. The dishes clanked in the rack. The faucet spewed water over the plates. Outside was the excited peep of an osprey. "They must have a fish," I told Mama as we walked to the deck. We could see two large black-and-white birds swooping into the nest on the flat-topped fir to the north of us. "What a commotion," she said. Then she turned to me. "Angela, I need to go home. I hate to cut this trip short, but there is so much to decide."

I knew she'd do this. Go home early.

She touched my hand lightly. I blinked back tears and tried to ignore them. But when I looked and saw she too was crying, I grabbed her. I felt a sob shake us, but I did not keep crying. "I'll call the airline," I said finally. "When do you want to go?"

"Tomorrow." Her cheeks were damp.

"Okay."

For whom were we grieving? What grief can lie like this upon a family? Is it grief inherited? Great Grandpa Gerad Galway never discussed his native Ireland. He never discussed it even though he was twenty years old when he arrived with a young son and wife, both of whom died shortly thereafter. Was it too painful to remember? Did he look away each time his sons said, tell us a story of when you were little, Daddy? Did he seal off the places and people he grieved, and in doing so, teach his sons and their sons, to seal off that which ached? Or was it that each successive grief compounded it, until there was nothing more to say? Great Grandpa's second wife died in childbirth when Grandpa was three. Grandpa didn't remember her except that his father had her hair cut after she died and woven by a neighbor into flowers, which he framed to hang in the parlor above the spot where she had last lain in rest.

Is grief indigenous to the prairies? Does it grow there like the black-eyed susans and purple prairie coneflower? Maybe grief is part of the silence, too. Did Gerad mistakenly blame the land for his losses, taking it out on the soil, the soil that enfolded his wives and children, the soil that in time would absorb him too? He took his plow and he ripped the earth into furrows and broke the furrows into clods, and then he planted grain, daring the earth to not grow it. The sweat made him feel better than the tears. And the earth complied. It grew his crops, offering tall slim corn plants and vast easy fields of honey-colored wheat and oats. This is the way he wielded a farm out of land that had known only wind and weather and insistent roots of prairie grass. Virgin prairie.

I would send my mother back to the prairie that was no virgin to grief. I called the toll free number for American Airlines. "Got you a flight tomorrow morning at 11," I said.

She nodded. We were on automatic. "Do you want anything washed," I continued. "I'm about to do a load."

"I've got two or three things." She disappeared down the steps to her room. Kristen watched me and gurgled. I watched the empty spot on the stairs where Mama disappeared.

When Gerad buried his second wife, they say he quit going to church and started frequenting the bar on the river. He left Grandpa and his brothers to do the evening chores, and would ride his horse five miles north until he came to the wooded curves of the Sangamon River. He'd stay there late, sometimes until the wee hours of the morning. Then he'd make his way back south, and fall asleep on the daybed in the kitchen until the sun rose and he again went out to meet his land.

But his land, as cooperative as it was, offered little solace. When he leaned on the plow handle or slumped against a shady tree trunk, he saw his loneliness reflected in an unbroken horizon that would not stop. West a mile was the Moffet house and east, a small cemetery. There was seldom any foot traffic or sound other than the soft, sad call of mourning doves and the clicking of insects. Grandpa said Gerad was a man of few words. So he soothed his pain with the liquid that made him forget wives and babies, hair flowers and Ireland.

I've never been to Ireland, but I've been told it's gentle and rolling, not hard and flat, that oceans keep the air cool and moist, and that there are no snakes. I always wondered about that, a place with no snakes. A place you can overturn any leaf, wallow in grasses, climb rocky ledges, and not worry about a serpentine form slipping away here or there or startling you with a quick hard bite. Gerad knew no snakes until he was twenty. Not until the prairie.

5

Mama returned with an arm load of laundry. "I have more than I thought," she said. "Let me do laundry this morning. I'll do it all."

"Okay," I answered. We were both happier when she was working.

I collected the boys' laundry from their room, which was dark, still having the shades drawn. I raised the shades before picking up anything, just in case. "This room smells like a gymnasium," Mama said earlier in the week. I raised a couple of windows, one on the west, one on the south, to get some cross ventilation.

Mama appeared at the door. "Think I'll give this room a good going over while you are doing laundry" I said. "You are right about its smelling like a gym."

"When I get this going I'll help you," she said. We were almost cheerful. I stripped the beds while she took the clothes to the basement. When she returned I let her help me turn the mattresses. I washed the baseboards and woodwork with an ammonia solution Mama made, while Mama washed windows. We turned on a radio talk show. A hummingbird buzzed the fuchsias outside the west window. We listened for Kristen, who napped in her room.

"Think I won't bother these desks," I said. "I'll have the boys clean them this evening."

"Jimmy used to have such a mess in his room," Mama said, wiping a rag over the mirror. "I'd want to get in there and clean the top of his desk, but your dad would always say, 'That's Jimmy's, let him take care of it.' So I did. And Jimmy always had a huge mess. His desk still looks just like it did then, except now it's in the middle of their living room. Poor Kate. Jimmy won't let her touch it, either."

I finished dusting the desk lamp and sniffed the air. "What makes that smell, anyway?" I asked.

"Sweat," Mama answered. "They certainly do a lot of rough housing in here." She pulled a stiff peanut butter crust from behind the dresser she was lemon oiling. "And old food!"

"They'll have mice in here!" I exclaimed.

"Mice and God knows what else!" Mama said. As she pulled the dresser out from the wall, she stopped.

"Angela, what is this?" She pointed to a large piece of dried material. I bent over it. Some animal had obviously relieved itself.

"I don't know," I said, "but it's way too large to be mice."

"Let's get out of here," Mama said, almost giggling. "We'll just close the door and let them vacuum this evening." Her face was girlish. "We're almost done anyway."

"Okay," I said, laughing. "If we find poop larger than a piece of rice, they have to clean it up!" Then we both laughed, relieved.

But we continued working, folding laundry between rooms, doing each room thoroughly and painstakingly. By midafternoon we were exhausted. I fixed Mama a glass of iced tea and myself some mineral water. We sat in the living room. Vacuum cleaner tracks curved gently outward from one corner of the rug. Kristen awakened from a short afternoon nap and nursed. Mama and I continued cleaning talk, about whether Spic and Span cleaned linoleum floors better than ammonia and about how Geraldine White cleaned silver with toothpaste. In a few minutes we heard the voices of Trent and Wheat. "Hi, Grandma, Hi, Mom!"

"Hello, Boys," we answered in unison.

"What's to eat?" Trent yelled. I heard him rifling the top of the refrigerator.

"Pretzels," I said. "Apples. Sandwiches. But hurry. I want you boys to get your room cleaned."

"Cleaned!" they yelled.

"Grandma and I did it mostly, so it's just finishing up. Straightening your desk. Making your beds. Vacuuming. Getting rid of the animal poop. What have you had in your room, anyway, that would have pooped under the dresser?"

"Beats me," said Trent.

"Could have been any one of a number of things," Wheat said.

"Well, whatever it was, and I don't want details, keep it out. It makes your room stink."

"I don't think it smells so bad," said Wheat.

"You've gotten used to it then," I said. "Finish eating and get to work. I want it done by supper."

"Mom's using her tough voice," Trent said to his grandmother on his way downstairs.

"She certainly is," Mama said. "She's spent just a little too long in that room of yours." Then she rocked back, resting her head on the chair. "It brings back memories."

"Of Moms bossing kids around?" asked Wheat.

"That's one way of seeing it," said Mama. "There are others."

"Name one."

"Go to your room, Wheat," I said. "You are delaying. And besides, Grandma is leaving tomorrow."

"Tomorrow?" said Wheat. "I thought she was staying three weeks."

"She was, but she feels she needs to get back early."

"Why?" Wheat turned to his grandmother.

"There's lots of decisions to be made." Mama said softly.

"But can't they wait? You'll miss the program at camp. You'll miss the skits."

"I know," she said sadly. "I'm sorry, too. But sometimes duty calls."

Trent returned. "What duty is calling?"

"Grandma is going back to get this business about the farm settled."

"Can't it be settled in two weeks?" Trent said.

"I just have to be there," Mama said, with more force. "It'll make me feel better."

"We'll make you feel better here," Wheat said.

"Grandma needs to go, Wheat. She needs to because that is how she feels, so stop badgering her."

"Okay," Wheat conceded. Then, "Want to spend some of your last hours with me in my room?"

"Wheat, Grandma has been working all day, and she's tired."

"That's okay, Angela, I'll go," Mama said, pushing herself to her feet. "We'll have that room finished in no time with the three of us working. The boys can do the heavy work."

So the three of them disappeared for half an hour, with Trent or Wheat reappearing periodically for a vacuum or a dust rag or clean sheets. As they returned, Trent said, "Mom, you wouldn't believe our room, it's never been that clean!" Mama had an arm around either boy's shoulder. All three were beaming. Tomorrow this time she'll be landing in St. Louis, I thought. A shaft of sunlight from the skylight backlit them, my mother and my sons, making halos of tiny hairs. I heard her laugh. "Maybe you boys will appreciate clean after all." Her voice echoed. I was filled with grief. I couldn't help thinking, this is such a peculiar way to say goodbye.

6

When Marcy first moved to Oregon, I thought I'd die. There had been a few warnings of an impending move, all which I had chosen to ignore. Two members of the weaving guild had moved to Oregon to look for land to raise sheep. Marcy talked of the increasing numbers of people in Sonoma County, of escalating land prices in California. Then one day, two years after I first met Marcy, she informed me a guild member had found some land and made an offer, which had been accepted.

When Marcy told me, I went into shock. "When?" I asked. What else was to be said?

"One month."

"You can't move to Oregon, I just met you."

Marcy laughed, but not too much. I could tell she was pulled by the enormity of her move, like I was when I moved to California. And I knew that you don't grieve too much when you've got to go. You might not leave.

"Why are you moving to Oregon?" I asked weakly.

"I've got to, Angela. I need more space around me. More quiet. I want an artists' community, one where we support each other in our art. This land is perfect for that. There are two houses on the land now, and several outbuildings. And there's a lot of room for sheep."

Our needs were different. I didn't want to see it, because I didn't want to let go of Marcy. Life is like this, is it not? One long separation? First you're merged, but you inhabit a body that will demand an ever growing space, and then it all begins. Or ends. I'm not sure which it is. When my first child Trent lay damp and bloody in my arms after his birth, eyes big and muddy, as crabby as this may sound, I didn't want to nurse him because I knew this would begin a new stage of our lives with his growing more apart from me. I could still feel the attached umbilical cord between my legs. I was torn apart, and the destruction had only just begun.

Marcy and I had a month to say goodbye. She showed me pictures of the land. We wove. I helped her pack the last two days. She owned surprisingly little. "The more you have, the more you have to work to keep it," Marcy said. She gave me her dresser and donated her dishes and an assortment of paperbacks to Goodwill. We mailed many boxes of weavings and yarns ahead, and shipped her large floor loom and a smaller portable one.

"Keep weaving," Marcy said. "Each time you pick up the beater to tap the yarns into place, each time you use the needle the way it's been used for ages, we are together, we all are together, weavers everywhere."

I was not consoled. But after she left, I longed for that time of the day in my studio, alone or joined, as you will, with the other weavers of the world and the ages, and with Marcy. From her, I had learned that each weaver is important to the whole. Although we learn to weave by weaving as it has always been done, our individualism comes forth only after we are proficient in the ancient practices of the craft. That is when we discover our genius. And that genius becomes yet another part of the larger weavers' tapestry.

7

Again, I am reminded of my moving to California. I had been here only a week when I decided to visit a prune farm. Nevada had left me weak and frightened, and I was homesick for you, Mama, and the earth. The want ad under Farm Supplies and Produce said, "Prunes, pick your own, 10 cents a pound," so I dialed the number, hoping, even assuming, that I would be recognized as family.

The woman on the phone sounded like Eva Barger. When Eva played the piano at Sunday school, her hands leaped a foot into the air between chords and usually came down on the right notes for the next chord. Her head swayed, blued-gray hair in tight waves, as her shoulders kept time.

This woman could be fierce competition for Eva. Her voice was forceful despite its raspiness. She didn't mince words. "Bring your own sacks, honey," she said, and she gave me the address, 213 Coffee Lane.

I was learning to get around Santa Rosa. I knew the main street now, the end with the cheap motels where I stayed my first three nights, and the other end with the trees and lawn of the Junior College campus. I followed her directions out of town, through residential streets and then to rundown farms.

The peeling paint showed the house was once painted white but now was mostly the worn gray of weathered redwood. A small barn and several sheds circled the driveway, all leaning and silver, except for one which had rusted metal sheets tacked to the sides. Knee-deep golden grass filled the yard and the prune orchard beyond.

She was sitting on the steps of a long porch that ran alongside the house. She was smaller than her voice, and even from a distance I could tell her deep brown curly hair was a wig that any gust of wind might send tumbling across the driveway like sagebrush. Totally absorbed in doing nothing, she did not appear to notice my arrival.

As I stepped from my car, I felt a lightness in my chest. Aunt Agnes lived alone on her farm too, but the grass was green and cut short to the earth, the house was white and in good repair, and the barns were red even though they were only used to store her sons' farm machinery. Aunt Agnes sat on her porch in a white wicker rocker. She waved the minute you turned into her lane.

But this woman was not Aunt Agnes, I reminded myself on my way up the broken walk, surreptitiously glancing at rusted green porch furniture beneath piles of magazines, cans, and clothing. Several saucers with flecks of dried food cluttered the base of the wooden porch steps. "Hello," I said.

She may have been very old. I could not tell. Her printed formless dress barely covered the rolled garters of the brown cotton hose squeezing her legs just below the knee. Her eyes finally focused on me. "Are you the one who called 'bout the prunes?" Vertical lines puckered her lips.

"Yes" I said, readjusting the grocery sacks under my arm. "Never had California prunes so thought I'd give 'em a try."

"Well, I got prunes all right," she said, "Just help yourself and then bring 'em here, and I'll weigh 'em for ya." She motioned to a small fruit scale on the floor of the porch almost covered by an avalanche of *Life* magazines.

I walked to the orchard. The ground was parched and cracked. Yellowed grass brushed my bare legs, making them itch. I wished I had worn jeans.

When I reached the trees and discovered no prunes on the branches, I felt like a green horn. Do you remember the time Mama's friend from Chicago visited and we laughed when she asked what grew on the green bushes in the soybean fields? We also let her pump a full two minutes at the well before we told her about priming the pump. We thought this was funny.

Suddenly I knew that I knew nothing about picking prunes. It was not like picking apples, or peaches, or apricots. The prunes were not on the tree. When I finally discovered them on the ground, I tasted one. The hard wrinkles hid a mouthful of summer dust. I spit it out, put three or four handfuls into one of the sacks, and called it quits.

As I returned to the house, I noticed the woman was still sitting on the steps, but just as I reached the porch, I stepped on something hard and round. When I glanced down, I saw an eighteen inch black and yellow garter snake writhing beneath my shoe. Reflexively, I screamed. The snake slithered into a tangled bed of forget-me-nots.

"So you're one of them," she said after a minute. "You probably even kill 'em." She laughed a humming laugh that caught in her throat and warbled, leaning toward me. "They guard you, you know. They guard you, and they guard the land. Kill 'em and you kill your very spirit!" Her false teeth clicked against the roof of her mouth.

Instinctively I moved backward a step, hoping the snake was long gone. "I got the prunes," I said, offering her my sack.

She watched me a long minute before taking it. "Why you don't have enough to weigh! What's wrong, prune pickin' too hard for ya? You young 'uns is all the same!" She placed the sack on the scales anyway. "Twenty cents," she said.

I handed the woman two dimes.

"Sure is dry in the orchard," I forced myself to say.

"You're damned right! It's August!" She almost lost her top plate of teeth but didn't seem to notice. "How long have you been in the state, anyway!" she said, moving her gaze to my license plate.

"Eight days." I shifted feet, ready to leave.

"You visitin'?"

"Going to school. Marine biology."

"Well, just make sure you go back to where you came from when you're done," she said, not totally unkindly. "Look at Santa Rose there. These days I can see it from my porch. They have no use for prunes anymore, not here. It don't pay to keep the orchards. S'pose they're gonna make me sell my land for more houses."

The atmosphere was oppressive. I took the sack with the prunes I would never eat, thanked her, and started down the walk. I breathed deeply, nauseated and homesick. The sight of my car relieved me. Again, I heard a soft warble, but dared not look back. Instead, I hurried to the car. The familiar chrome handle in my palm welcomed me and the old car smell enfolded me as I slipped into my seat.

I understand about yearning for return. I never felt it as strongly as I did that day. I hated the dryness, the dustiness, the witheredness. Most of all, I hated how deeply disturbed I felt. I drove off, breathing deep for the slightly oily smell of my Volvo.

8

I watched the loading ramp being pulled from my mother's plane. Then the plane slowly moved backward, turned, and taxied toward the runway. I watched it race the runway, then ease into the air, wheels tucking into its body. Soon it disappeared into a clear blue sky. I imagined my mother's tear-stained face peering through the elliptical window, searching for that place where she left the earth. Now she'd yearn for me too. I pushed Kristen through the nondescript hall that could be any airport. All around us people were leaving or returning, meeting or being left: a young mother with a newborn met by an older couple who looked very much like her; a couple intertwined in a corner until arms and legs belong to either.

On the way to the airport, I had told Mama a snake story I read in the paper, hoping to lift the grief that had settled over us like cellophane. A man was arrested for taking his boa constrictor through surveillance in a suitcase. "What do you have in your suitcase," the surveillance officer asked. "My boa constrictor," the man answered. They opened the suitcase anyway, and, finding a very large snake, arrested him for trying to take a dangerous snake on the plane.

"Oh, heavens!" Mama said, horrified. "I never thought of someone taking snakes on planes."

I had not meant to scare her, only jolt us both out of grief. "I'm sure they don't," I added quickly "or rarely, anyway. They would have to be declared."

"That's why they'd sneak them," she said, too seriously. "They are afraid of getting charged more if they declare them."

"Mama, not that many people travel with snakes."

"It doesn't take that many." And I noticed her looking at every suitcase in the check-in line, and later at the surveillance station. She even asked the officer if he could detect animals in suitcases with the x-ray. He insisted on examining her carryon and purse, carefully pulling out each item, while Mama looked on, humiliated.

I remember this now, already missing Mama. Suddenly I thought I heard the prune lady's warbled laugh. Was she here? I looked around quickly. Several men in uniform stood behind me, clean shaven and baby faced. The young mother's greeters held the infant outside the women's restroom. A man in a pinstriped suit sat in a plastic chair reading a Denver newspaper. I saw no one else. "You kill the guardian, you kill the spirit," I heard the old woman say.

Just how does the spirit of the land sustain itself? The prune lady is not the only one who talked of snakes as being earth guardians. Marcy told me that the earth has spirits that guard places, and that the spirit of a place is embodied in a snake. She said this spirit insures the continuity of the place's existence.

Now my mother was returning to the farm where four generations of farmers have purged the land of snakes. The timber rattler has totally disappeared from your fields—and I must stop calling them that. They do not belong to you anymore.

Did we kill one snake too many? Was there one in this century-long massacre that was a little more vivid, clothed in light, a little more alive than the rest? Would our farm still be healthy and intact had you not killed it? Again, I think of the prune lady. Her farm is now a development of cracker box condos, each painted the same as the next. What happened to her farm's guardian?

9

The freeway home was remarkably clear. Kristen slept. I drove the prevailing speed, lost in reverie until I took the exit west. Kristen awakened when I approached a stop sign, so I pulled over on a quiet stretch to nurse her.

I felt lifeless still. The farm being sold. You dead. We were no longer a farming family. My eyes rested on rolling yellow hills dotted here and there by cattle. I closed my eyes and expansive fields of grain stretched before me, fields worked by you, Uncle Dan, and Uncle Will. I was riding my bicycle early evening through dirt lanes, barelegged and free. It was the land of plenty in those years. It was how I defined myself, and later, how I propelled outwards, like a swimmer pushing against the side of a pool. The illusion was it would always be there. It was the Mother and the Father, the thing that lived on as wives and husbands and children and fathers and mothers died.

Kristen watched me intently as she sucked. I smiled. She smiled back. Milk raced from her mouth over puffy cheeks and down her chin. I wiped it away with a finger. She pulled away and articulated a loud, "Gah!" "Gah!" I repeated. She laughed, then fervently began nursing again, eyes still fixed on mine. A car whizzed by. A cow mooed. A raven circled overhead.

Harvest

FIVE

The garter snake usually mates at or near the wintering site. The male has minute sensory organs, little barbels, on his chin. He rubs these along the back of an acquiescent female as his body passes over hers. As a result of this mating, the female brings forth live young late in the summer. The number in a brood varies greatly; sometimes there are only twelve snakelets, though there are records of as many as one hundred. Probably the average is fifty or sixty.

Will Barker, *Familiar Reptiles and Amphibians of America*

1

In the spring of the year I met Jake, I practically moved in with him, though you never knew this, and took the only two marine biology courses offered that semester: Kelp Forest Ecology and Marine Invertebrate Zoology, although I had no idea what I wanted to do with the course work when I finished.

Everything I did, I did with passion. I made love with Jake with passion. I talked passionately about women's rights with Marcy. Dr. Witzweier's lectures were a source of passionate inspiration, albeit more as metaphors than as science. Only when I got your occasional letter from home, "Will you be back by Father's Day?" or "Joanne Simpson was asking about when you'd get back," only then did I feel a cooling. I tried not to think about it too long. "I don't know yet," I'd tell you. "I just don't know." Gradually, you quit asking.

That was the spring when Dr. Witzweier informed me he had received a huge grant from NRI for a research project in Mexico and Panama and that he needed two assistants for a summer trip. He was about to detail the research when we were interrupted by a phone call. "Can you go, Miss Galway?" he asked, holding his hand over the receiver. "It will be the last three weeks of July. Your room, board, and travel, of course, will be paid."

I was flattered. "Yes!" I said, exuberantly. "I'd love to!"

That evening I called you. "I'm going to Mexico and Panama this summer, Dad! And I'm getting paid for it. Dr. Witzweier asked me to travel as one of his research assistants."

"What are you researching?" you asked, noticeably hiding your disappointment.

"Uh-tidal pool life in the tropics, I expect. I'll know more later. He didn't have time to go into it."

Later that evening Jake asked the same question. I delayed telling him about the trip until after we made love. It was an unseasonably warm night, so we had the window open. I could hear Jake's neighbors arguing next door.

"Research what?" he asked.

"I'm not sure yet, he didn't have time to go into it," I explained. "But it involves tropical waters."

Jake chuckled.

"Why are you laughing?"

"Angela, sometimes you scare me. I can't believe you'd agree to this when you have no idea what's involved. Do you have any idea what field research can entail? Once I got stuck on the Farallons a month dissecting seal carcasses. We had to analyze everything, stomach contents, intestinal parasites." He turned onto his side and pushed himself up on his elbow. "But it's one of the things I love about you, too. You are game for anything."

I felt a little uneasy. "Why don't you come too," I said.

"I can't. I'm teaching Witzweier's marine biology while he's gone."

"Oh," I sobered. I suddenly felt alone. What if I had to analyze animal shit? Or cut up seals?

The next morning I went straight to Dr. Witzweier's office. He had just arrived and was filling acrylic containers with sea water. *"Guten Morgen!"* he greeted me.

"Good morning, Dr. Witzweier," I said. "I've been wondering since we talked yesterday what kind of research we will be doing in July."

"Oh, very exciting, Miss Galway, and very important! We will be studying the migration patterns of *Pelamis platurus*. There is concern they may spread through the Panama Canal should it be made sea level. This is just the beginning of a three-year study to chart the territory of these animals."

"Will we be dissecting them?" I asked.

"Oh, I think not this trip, anyway. This trip we will study them from a hot air balloon. They collect in groups of thousands of individuals. We will survey the size and exact location of these aggregations. Next fall we will mark individuals, but not this trip."

I did not ask what *Pelamis platurus* were. It seemed like a stupid question, and I thought if I were several hundred feet above them, it wouldn't matter anyway. "Okay," I said, relieved.

"Mr. Murdock will also be going," Dr. Witzweier continued. "I like to expose my most interested students to the joys and rigors of scientific work."

I felt the burning excitement I had come to know so well this year. Puerto Vallarta, Baja, Acapulco. Musical names, names that had been only two dimensional puzzle pieces on a world map. It was like my drive here: Kansas City, Denver, Elko. I shuddered, scratch Elko. Reno, San Francisco. Cities I'd heard of, studied about, but which existed far outside of my safe web until recently.

That afternoon I met Jake in the student union for coffee. "It's not cutting up seals, it's studying the migration patterns of *Pelamis platurus*," I stated.

Jake looked stunned. "Those are highly poisonous. One venomous bite and you're done for. Furthermore, I can't believe you would do that after your reaction at my parents'."

I must have looked stunned too. "What are you talking about?" It was only a few weeks since the incident at his parents, and we were both still a little touchy about it.

"You don't know what *Pelamis platurus* are? " Jake sounded incredulous. "Angela, those are sea snakes!"

"Sea snakes?"

"Yellow-bellied sea snake!" he whooped with laughter.

"Stop it! I mean it! Stop it! It's not funny." Two or three students at a nearby table stared.

"I know," Jake said, visibly trying to calm down. "I know. But Angela, you sign up for a research trip, having no idea it's to study a very poisonous snake, when you would not spend another night in my parents' house with snakes in captivity!"

I gave him a cool look, gathered my books together. "Class," I said. "I've got five minutes to get there."

Jake was trying not to laugh. "See ya!" he said.

Jake's reaction did spur me to do some reading on sea snakes. Although few humans are bitten and die from sea snake bites, sea snakes are numerous in the east Pacific. Because they are so poisonous, they have few, if any, predators; when they are introduced into new territory, they are preyed upon by various species, but this doesn't last long because those species learn to stay away or die.

In retrospect, maybe I should have taken a hint from those species who learned to stay away. Instead, I was cheered on by Marcy, who insisted that, at last, I was confronting my fate in meeting the sea snake! I soothed my mind by telling myself the study was at some distance, having no idea what a slick in the ocean filled for miles by hundreds of thousands of snakes looked like. I didn't picture the writhing and knotting and frenetic feeding movements of these snakes. If I had, I would never have gone.

"These snakes, poisonous as they are, are helpless on land," Dr. Witzweier said on our flight to Puerto Vallarta. "If they are washed ashore, they might try rolling, but they are stranded and become dehydrated and die. They are dependent on the currents to carry them. They may travel aggressively at a speed of a meter a second, but it is only for short distances. So they float on the ocean currents and thousands end up in slicks, or places the currents intersect. That's what we are looking for."

They sounded deceptively helpless.

We landed in Puerto Vallarta, our first stop, on Sunday evening just as the sun was setting. The white stucco buildings gleamed like teeth around and down the hills. The ocean lay turquoise and tranquil for what seemed like half the earth. *"Por favor, llevanos a la casa de Frank,"* Dr. Witzweier said to the taxi cab driver. Please take us to The House of Frank.

The cab ride was circuitous along cobblestone streets lined with beggars and street merchants putting away their wares. Canadians and Americans sat in open-air restaurants eating frijoles and enchiladas. "Tacos!" a young boy called from a square grill on the sidewalk.

The cab stopped abruptly in front of a white stucco building. Harry and I climbed out as Dr. Witzweier paid the driver. Then the three of us unloaded several large cases of instruments and our backpacks.

"Well, here we are!" Dr. Witzweier charged ahead through the archway into a large courtyard. A graceful tree stretched branches over several tables on the bricked patio, and two men and a woman lounged at one of the tables.

"Buenos Dias!" Dr. Witzweier greeted them.

"Buenos Dias!" they returned.

"Is Frank here?"

"He's across the street," said one of the men. "Have a seat and wait."

As we set down the luggage, Harry returned to the street to get the last two cases of instruments. Dr. Witzweier asked the students about the weather which had been unbelievably hot, and about the inn which had been sparsely populated. Many American and Canadian students and adventurous travelers frequented Frank's because it was clean and cheap.

Frank was not above putting strangers together in a room to make space for more occupants. When he returned, he and Dr. Witzweier bargained a few minutes about room arrangements. First Frank wanted to put all three of us together in a large room with two double beds on the second floor. "It is not proper," Dr. Witzweier insisted. Then Frank wanted to put me with the woman student in the courtyard. "Unacceptable!" Dr. Witzweier said. "We need two rooms, three beds!" Frank settled on the large room upstairs with the two double beds and a smaller adjacent room, just as Dr. Witzweier requested in the first place. We took our luggage to our rooms, then walked to a nearby restaurant to get dinner. The waiter brought us each Tecate with fresh lime and salt, and I ordered the first Mexican food I had ever had.

During dinner we discussed the work. We would fly over the ocean in a hot air balloon to locate slicks where aggregations of snakes could be found. We would plot these areas. On later trips snakes would be collected and marked. Individuals would be traced to see if they traveled from one area to another or if they were territorial.

I will not be on those trips, I thought as I asked, "How will you collect them?"

"With snake tongs," Dr. Witzweier said, "and with care. They do bite. If you are in the water with them you wear a wet suit. Their fangs seldom penetrate wet suits. We notch the tail only a little, a particular spot, depending on where the individual was caught." He drank the last of his beer. He had only one. "Are we finished?" he asked, looking at my half full plate.

"Yes," Harry and I said, standing to leave. Dr. Witzweier paid the waiter and then we walked through the dark cobblestone street to our inn.

My room was simple. The bed was surrounded by a film of mosquito netting draped from a canopy above. There was no window, but many four inch square vent holes were staggered at intervals above eye level. Two lizards hung on the wall near the ceiling.

It was hot and humid. I undressed, brushed my teeth, and lay on the bed. My sweat did not evaporate.

I missed Jake. If he were here, I'd enjoy this trip, I thought. Tears came, and, as I had on the Humboldt coast, I cried into my pillow until it was soaked with tears and I fell asleep.

At five A.M. I was awakened by the braying of a donkey in the courtyard next to my bedroom wall. The room was barely lit by an impending dawn. There was something inside me that felt wide awake. The room with its drape of white cotton gauze felt at once familiar. A rooster crowed. How would I weave this, I wondered? Goldens, shades of goldens and yellows that fade into whites, hot whites, light whites, billowy whites like sails of ships that blow across oceans...

Then I completely awoke, sitting bolt upright. What have I done? It is so strange to me now that I did not consider that until then. What have I done? Blowing across oceans in balloons by air currents, like sea snakes drifting in ancient water intersections. Floating above masses of snakes... What was I thinking? I must go home.

I'll call Jake. He'll meet me at the airport. Dr. Witzweier can hire a local person. Frank will help him find someone. I'll pay my way back. I'll fly stand by. I got up and dressed quickly, pulling on a pair of shorts, sandals, and a woven yoke blouse Marcy made me. There was a knock at the door.

"*Guten Morgen*, Miss Galway!" He stood there with two cups of coffee.

"Hi," I said, a little guiltily. I took the cup and sipped the rich coffee. "What's on the agenda?"

"Our maiden voyage!" Dr. Witzweier said. I took another sip and decided the coffee was bitter. Then I took a last look at my room, and stepped out, pulling the door shut behind me.

Harry was already waiting downstairs in the courtyard. "Sleep well, Angela?" he asked, grinning.

"Pretty hot," I said.

"Mexico is a land of heat," Dr. Witzweier said. His eyes glazed the tops of the white stucco buildings visible from the courtyard. Something was different about him, and I could not place it at first. He looked more boyish. Suddenly it hit me. "Dr. Witzweier, you shaved your beard!"

"Ah, yes, for the tropics," he said. "It is far too hot to have a beard in the tropics." He seemed pleased I noticed.

We finished our coffee and placed the cups on a small table to the side of the courtyard. The sky had lightened considerably. "Well, let us begin!" said Dr. Witzweier. "We are to meet Philip on the beach at 6 A.M."

We walked side by side down a street that tilted toward the ocean. Burros were already at work carrying their burdens of large gray stones in packs that hung heavy either side of their backs. All day at any hour they could be seen walking in trains carrying their loads, clop, clop, over the streets, up the hill and then, unburdened, returning.

As we turned into a narrow alley for two blocks and then back toward the ocean, we saw a rainbow colored balloon just over the last row of buildings. "It's here!" Dr. Witzweier said, walking even faster. Philip was ready to go when we reached him. "All aboard!" he greeted us.

The woven basket which would carry us rested in the white sand of the beach. It was shockingly small. Philip helped me climb in first, then I took the equipment as Dr. Witzweier handed it to me. The others followed and Philip untied the ropes. The balloon lifted us from the ground.

The sun was balloon level as we rose and floated away from the beach. I could see a dozen burros heading up a hill. There were more people on the streets. Silently, we floated seaward. The day was clear and still.

After half an hour Dr. Witzweier began to peruse the waters with his binoculars. Harry and I set up some survey equipment. I pulled a notebook out of the case, and reviewed the directions. We were to record the width of the slicks, our exact location, and the time and date. We decided to take turns. At first Harry would record and I would read the survey information.

Half an hour became an hour, and then an hour and a half. We could no longer see land. "Great day for this," Philip said. "No wind at all. We should head down in fifteen minutes, however, to beat the afternoon breezes."

Dr. Witzweier stood, binoculars on the horizon. "Philip," he said, "Quick! Can we go more toward that rift in the water? Oh, yes! At last! My god! Miss Galway! Mr. Murdock, we have found them! And look at them!"

At first it looked like a seam that had frayed loose, darker and more alive than the rest of the ocean. But as the balloon carried us closer, it became quite clear we were floating over thousands and thousands of snakes, writhing and knotting and wiggling. I stood frozen. There was no where to run. "My god," Harry said quietly.

"Have you ever seen anything like it?" Philip said. He had, of course, though this is the first time he'd actually sought them out.

I said nothing. "Get the readings, Miss Galway," Dr. Witzweier said. "Philip, can we follow this slick south? How far does this extend?"

"We've got about ten minutes until we need to go down," Philip said. "Our boat is on the way. We'll see how far we can get. Get a position reading, and we'll start here tomorrow."

I dropped a ball point pen over the basket by accident. It fell into the middle of the wiggling mass. Its arrival was met by a few seconds of wild activity around the point of contact.

"What was that?" Dr. Witzweier called, binoculars still glued to his eyes.

"My ball point pen," I said. "It fell."

"They want it," laughed Harry. "Look at 'em go!"

I dug a pencil from the bottom of my pack and wrote down the figures Harry read off. Dr. Witzweier was recording descriptions of the snakes' activities on a small pad of paper. I recorded a second reading and a third. I tried to pretend we were not twenty-five feet above a sea alive with some of its most forbidding inhabitants. I did not look down.

"Make sure and note our position here, Miss Galway," Dr. Witzweier said. "This is where I want to begin tomorrow."

"22° 50' North, 107° 32' West" Harry called out. I wrote down the numbers.

"Let's go!" Philip said. The balloon jerked as it began its journey up. A slight breeze caught us. The balloon drifted like a phantom. Dr. Witzweier and Philip talked excitedly about the find as Philip radioed for the large flat boat that was to collect us. Harry and I were silent as we watched it approach. Our shadow was almost directly below us as we watched the deck approach us. The balloon landed with a jolt. Philip hopped out almost immediately and grabbed my hand. "Just leap over the side, " he said. "I'll catch you."

I pulled myself up over the edge and leaped onto deck. The others followed. When the boat reached the shore thirty minutes later, Dr. Witzweier jumped from the deck, exclaiming, "Mr. *Pelamis platurus* is here to meet us!" He walked to a dark snake with a molted yellow tail six feet from the waterline. "Dead. Probably due to dehydration." He rolled it with a stick to show us its flat tail and yellow underbelly. Then he turned to Philip, who was busy packing up the balloon. "Tomorrow at six then?"

"Tomorrow morning at six." Philip shook Dr. Witzweier's hand, then waved to Harry and me.

"Let's go eat!" Dr. Witzweier said, and we each picked up a bag of equipment, and started up the beach.

We spent the afternoons eating, napping, and, when the midday heat faded, going over the data collected in the mornings. It was unbearably hot. There were no fans, though evening breezes helped. Dr. Witzweier remained undaunted by the weather. Harry sweated a lot, beads of perspiration lining his eyes by noon and remaining there until after dark.

By the fourth day, we were oblivious to the facts of the situation. I managed by concentrating on my tasks. 22° 50' N, 107° 32' W. 36 meters wide. 19° 36' N, 107° 14' W, 45 meters wide. 19° 19' N, 107° 25' W, 1726 meters wide. "My god!" was all Dr. Witzweier said. "Have you ever seen so many snakes?" I ignored the question and kept writing down the numbers Harry read.

The day was different from the first three. By the time we had been in the air two hours, I felt a slight breeze cool my face. Within five minutes, Philip announced we needed to come down. The wind was picking up. We had grown used to unusually calm mornings and this came as a surprise to all of us.

At the time we were over a large slick we had discovered the day before. The aggregation itself was a mile wide and extended for miles in either direction. It had grown considerably from the day before, so Dr. Witzweier was particularly interested in recording the rate of increase and the activity of the individuals. By dropping a monitor tied to a rope into the snakes, we could also determine how deep the aggregation was. Dr. Witzweier was preparing to lower the monitor over the edge of the basket when Philip told us that he had radioed for the boat to collect us. "Do we have time for a reading?" Dr. Witzweier asked. "It will take about ten minutes."

"Sure," Philip said.

"How close can you get us to the water?" Dr. Witzweier asked.

"Ten feet, maybe, let's see…" and we began to slowly lower over the writhing raft of snakes.

Suddenly we dropped. It was the kind of drop that leaves your stomach behind. "We're going down!" Philip yelled.

I don't know what the others did. They never told me. But I screamed. It was a mindless scream, a black scream, cold as a snake's gaze. I screamed and I watched the snakes. They oozed out of the water like enormous maggots. I saw all the snakes I'd ever seen, the garter snakes in the rose bushes, the South American species roaming Lloyd and Irene's house, the rubber replica Tim Willard chased me with years ago. I saw Jimmy holding the king snake in the corn crib, and I saw bales of hay turn into snake infested bundles. I saw Hershel falling backward, grabbing the snake in his overalls, drowning in terror. I screamed out of that terror, and as I screamed I realized I screamed alone. I knew as surely as I knew I would drop into the water that you couldn't save me. There was no one to save me.

"It wasn't a free fall, Miss Galway," Dr. Witzweier told me later, "the balloon was still partly inflated, it let us down easy." But to me we fell like a bomb.

The gondola hit the water first and tipped, spilling us. I screamed as the water plunged in on us. I screamed even as I swallowed mouthfuls of sea water.

At first I didn't feel the bite, but I felt the snake. It didn't release its grip on my right thigh for some time. I felt it flopping against me. "He's biting me! He's biting me!" I spurted between screams. I thought I would drown.

Dr. Witzweier grabbed me by the back of my blouse. "Ms. Galway, calm down, you're okay," he yelled. "The snakes are gone. Swim, tread water. Survive, Miss Galway!"

Philip managed to call for help on his radio before the gondola submerged. A helicopter arrived in what seemed like hours. Someone lowered a rope to us, and Dr. Witzweier tied it around my waist. Then I was pulled into the belly of the helicopter. "Radio the hospital," Dr. Witzweier called to the rescuers. "She's been bitten!" I watched as the rope was lowered for the others. The balloon lay wilted on a placid sea.

I did not see the bite until after I was in the helicopter. Sure enough, there was a small spot on my thigh. "You will be okay, Miss Galway," Dr. Witzweier said. "Very few bites are venomous, and we are taking you to the hospital."

We waited two hours at the hospital to see if I developed symptoms of a venomous bite: stiffness in my neck, muscular pains, giddiness, or difficulty in speaking. We were left in an examining room made of concrete blocks painted white. I was instructed to rest. The bite was cleaned by a small nurse who kept saying, "*Pobrecita!*" I said nothing.

"If you don't talk, we won't know if you have difficulty in speaking," Harry chirped.

"Shut up," I said as good naturedly as I could muster. "I'm stunned."

"I got to keep you talking," Harry said, "so we can tell if you start slurring your words or get too giddy. At least you didn't have to cut your leg off."

"What?"

"Skin divers have done that," Harry said. "If they are out away from help and get bitten on a finger or hand, they've been known to cut that hand off."

"Mr. Murdock, that is quite enough," Dr. Witzweier said. "Miss Galway is already frightened. Besides, she may have saved us."

"What?" Harry and I both looked at him in surprise. His shirt and shorts were still slightly damp, though he looked as vigorous as ever.

"Her screaming," Dr. Witzweier said. "Miss Galway, you may have scared them off. They dove to get away from us. You may have saved our lives."

At the moment I didn't appreciate the full breadth of this. "I want to go home," I said. It just popped out.

Dr. Witzweier looked at me a little sadly. "When we get done here, we'll get something to eat, and rest, and then, of course, if that is what you still want, we'll look into a flight."

It is what I wanted. I had no symptoms, so I was released. Dr. Witzweier was to keep a close watch over me for the next few hours. We ate as if we had never eaten before and I slept long and hard until morning. And while they made a trip to the slick, this time in the thirty foot boat with rented equipment, I drank coffee in the court-yard at Frank's with the Canadians and arranged my return flight at 7:57 P.M. that evening.

Somewhere on the way down to the Pelamis, or on the way back up, I decided not to major in marine biology. "I'm not a researcher," I told Dr. Witzweier. With a nod of his head, he silently agreed. But he added, "Mr. *Pelamis platurus* took quite a liking to you, Miss Galway. You survived his bite." I shivered, smiling slightly.

I flew home to California, not looking down. I shut the blind on my window and closed my eyes anticipating Jake's embrace at the airport. What would I tell him? His concern would override his righteousness, at least for a while. He probably would not say, *I told you so!* I'd show him the wound on my thigh. He'd look at it tenderly, pull me even closer, kiss my forehead. And then, I'd weave. All I wanted to do was weave. And that is what I did.

2

Tricia, our day care provider, had a snake in the entry court of her yard. She told me after we'd been going there for two years. "But don't worry," she reassured me, "it only comes out at noon to sun on the path." She said it lived under the flagstones stacked by the entry and that she had not told the children. She was sure that they would bother it.

In August of that year, she told me she saw innumerable tiny snakes and that they squirmed from under the flagstones. She said there must have been a hundred. The children collected them in glass jars and carried them in pockets. A hundred snakes are too many to be kept secret.

The small black and yellow striped snake seemed almost innocuous in the hands of Wheat then five. "See Mom?" he yelled as I walked in the gate. He was running full speed toward me. "I caught a snake!"

"Stop!" I screamed.

Wheat stopped in his tracks, though his face was still filled with delight. A snakelet wiggled in his fat palm. He held the head gently with his thumb and forefinger. "We found it in the sand pile, and I caught it! All by myself!"

"Oh?" I managed, feigning delight. Then... "Don't come a step closer." I said it instead of screaming. Remembering Jake's admonitions about imparting my fear of snakes to the boys, I quickly added, "Just stand where you are and let me take a look. What a tiny head he has."

Wheat touched a finger to the tongue which was darting in and out rapidly. Then he stroked the entire body with his finger. "I want to take him home," he said. "James said you can keep 'em in a cage. Let me put him in your purse."

"No!" I shrieked. He eyed me, surprised. "Snakes don't go in purses," I explained, more calmly. "They might get hurt."

"Okay. Here, hold him while I go get a jar."

"No! Stay right where you are."

"Why?"

"We can't take a snake home. It might die. We don't know how to care for snakes. They are far happier in the spots they were born in. It is fun holding it, but let it go and let it grow up where it was born."

"James says cats will eat it. He said cats eat most baby snakes because zillions of snakes are born and only a few grow up. Oh please, Mom, please? Let's save this snake, please? I'll take care of him, I promise. James will show me how."

"Wheat, we aren't talking about a cat or a dog. We aren't even talking about a hamster. We are talking about a snake. Very few people have snakes as pets. There's a good reason for that."

Tears welled in Wheat's eyes. "What's the reason?"

"Because they are wild animals!" I said, too triumphantly. "Because they live best outside. The mother snake chooses the place to have them that is a good place for baby snakes to eat and sleep and sun. And it is not a smelly cage, either. No mother snake would choose a smelly cage for her babies."

"I'd clean the cage," he said sadly. But I'd won this battle. He walked back to the sand pile and crouched as he released the snakelet into the sand. "Goodbye, Otis," he said.

I had not won the war, however. It was only days before I heard an excited "Mom! I caught a snake!" at the door of our kitchen. And this time it wasn't a snakelet. It was the full eighteen inch garden variety that my grandmother screamed at forty years ago. "She was in the garden!" Wheat said, breathless. "Mom, can you believe it?!? Our garden is the right kind of place for snakes!"

Damn Jake. That was all I could think. Damn Jake. It's his fault. If he had taken away those mating snakes seven years ago when I first saw them, as you would have done, it wouldn't have come to this. Now, at an average of fifty snakes an August from one snake alone, we've had a minimum of 350 snakes born in the garden since that summer. And that's a conservative number.

The summer that Jake and I bought our house, we rototilled a small patch of earth below our south deck to grow tomatoes, peas, and lettuce. The patch received morning sun only, and it was questionable if our crops would thrive, but we planted them anyway. Every morning as I drank a cup of tea, I would go down to the deck, bask in the sun, and check the garden's progress. I was delighted one morning to notice tips of lettuce peeking up from one furrow. I finished my cup and then carefully worked the soil around each leaf with a trowel.

One morning as I leaned against the deck breathing deep for a whiff of the sweet earth, I saw what appeared to be a Medusa head laying in the lettuce. I couldn't believe my eyes. But sure enough, there was a pile of snakes slithering over and around each other in the two inch high lettuce. My reflexive scream was still automatic, even though after my immersion in the sea snakes I was beginning to get the idea there was no help, that I was in this alone. But nevertheless, I still screamed, and when I looked again it was only in time to catch two or three tails disappearing into the sweet peas.

"I want you to get those snakes," I said to Jake that evening.

"And what do you want me to do with them? Kill them?"

"No, of course not." I had worked with Dr. Witzweier too long for that. "I want you to take them away. Dump them in some out-of-the-way place. I just don't want them here, breeding."

But Jake was not convinced. "No," he said.

"No, what?"

"No, I will not catch three or four snakes in our garden and take them away. If you want them caught, you catch them."

I didn't, of course. It was out of the question. Where I came from women do not catch snakes. Certainly I do not. And it was out of the question to kill them, even if I chose to pursue them enough for that. Nothing is without its consequences. Besides, snakes are hard to kill.

So I did nothing except stop going into the garden, and since nothing is without its consequences our garden became a snake's haven, brambly, overgrown and undisturbed by human feet or hoes. There was plenty of morning sun, but no overbearing midday heat. Even our old snake-eating cat died soon thereafter.

Since nobody or nothing killed them, they continued to live there and breed until, in my mind, at least, our garden was a tangle of garter snakes. I imagined snakes plump as visions hanging from the limbs of the fruit trees, impregnating the undergrowth of the vines entwining our house, soon en-webbing our property like the aggregations off Puerto Vallarta.

It was my fate. That's what Marcy had said. It was my fate that Wheat lined the deck railing with jars, each with a small wiggling snake. It was my fate when he caught the momma of them and wore her like a necklace, when he smelled like snake musk as I bent to kiss him in his covers.

"You smell like snake," I said.

"Probably Vera," he said.

"Vera?" What?

"I caught Vera for a while this afternoon," he explained. "She must have got some of her musk on me."

"Haven't you washed?" I asked.

"I washed my hands," he said. "She probably got my neck and face, no, I bet my neck."

I had kissed snake musk. Oddly, in recognizing this, I felt ancient mystery vibrate within me.

I called Marcy. She laughed when I told her. "Maybe you are a reincarnation of the maiden in the story of Kolowissi!" she said.

"Am I dirtying up some sacred pool?" I asked.

"Maybe …or maybe it was just a ploy. Maybe Kolowissi fell in love with the maiden when he saw her bathing in his pool, so he seduced her anyway he could."

This was a new angle on the story. There was a long pause. I was thinking.

"For some reason, in life, the snake has chosen you," Marcy added. "You met it in a violent confrontation," referring, of course, to the sea snake mishap, "and you survived. You have some of its power."

"That's what Dr. Witzweier said." I felt so exasperated. "But what does it mean? And am I cursed to have this happen time and again, to be swamped in snakes?"

Now Marcy was quiet. I knew that she was also thinking. "Maybe the God who created us in his own image was a boa, after all," she said finally. "So we learn in coils, or spirals. Repeated experience is God reflected."

I found her words strangely comforting.

3

I can see now that after the sea snake experience, I went into suspension. I did finish a degree in general biology. Not knowing what else to do, I got a teaching credential and then substituted in several junior and senior highs. But my heart was not in it. Although I wanted to be an inspired teacher, my students remained bored. They took advantage of my in-expertise by giggling, throwing paper wads, and saving frog genitals from a dissection for the English teacher. I hated substituting.

It was around this time that Jake and I were married in a redwood forest by a minister with a mail-order license. We told you he was a priest, and he was, of sorts. You and Mama did not come, something I always regretted. There were reasons, of course, as there always are. Field work. Chores. Oh, well.

Jake and I got our first official apartment together. The days I didn't substitute, I spent weaving. Jake got a job teaching at the junior college and then the university. Gradually the schools stopped calling me early mornings, and Jake said we were fine on his salary. So I wove all day until I had babies.

But I could not let go of my weavings. A local gallery owner asked to handle them. "They'd sell," he said. But he did not understand that they were more than weavings. Even I did not know I was making the fabric of my life, pulling together discordant threads, desperately trying to hold the whole in my heart while weaving each particular. The weavings were not expendable. Too much in life is expendable. Not my weavings.

"It's not the cloth," Marcy told me once. "The cloth is like anything else. It builds up and becomes a burden. Let go of it, or unravel it, just keep weaving. The process is what is important. The process, and the *inner* fabric."

But I could not let the weavings go. There's just so much else in life that we have to relinquish.

4

Jimmy decided to sell our family farmland to Marvin Hobbs whose own land abutted the north forty, negotiating what he felt was a fair price. He set a date to sell the farm machinery at public auction in

February, a time before spring work began. The notices put in the papers for miles around brought buyers from 200 miles away. "Jim Galway attended many auctions and kept everything," the notice read. "Something here for everyone!"

These days a farm sale is a funeral of sorts, not only for the farmer who is selling out or has died, but also for the continuance of the small farm. Everyone who comes knows it. For most, it is only a matter of time until their own farm machinery and land will be up for auction. Each sale, usually a consolidation and the loss of a farming family, leans on the economy of the small town nearby. The main street in Flat Rock is lined with darkened storefront windows, like lost teeth. The Flat Rock schools are now consolidated with Macon's, our basketball rivals when I was in school, and Flat Rock no longer has a grocery store.

I returned with Kristen the week before to help Jimmy prepare and to be with Mama. Dorothy came too, and although Jimmy really was the one to do the sorting, Dorothy and I helped arrange smaller items on flatbed trailers: wrenches, hammers, shovels, bolts and nails, your wood working tools, chains, grease guns, gear pullers, vices, battery chargers, bench grinders, and antique tools of Gerad's and his son, our grandfather. We got a dumpster and filled it with the obvious trash, but most of the items would sell.

Meanwhile, Jimmy pulled out the farm machinery and parked it along the driveway and around the cribs: the 1928 "D" John Deere, the 1976 John Deere, the disk, the harrow, the chisel plow, the grain drills and barge wagons, the 500 gallon pull sprayer, trailers: all archaic in this day of industrial farming.

Mama cried easily. She was still living in the house, although she was preparing to move to a small two-bedroom bungalow in town. Jimmy and Kate would move into the farm house. Mama and Jimmy decided to keep the tractor that you bought when you and Mama were first married, which Jimmy would use to farm the acreage we were keeping around the house; we would keep enough implements to do this minimal farming. All of the rest was to be sold.

The morning of the sale, the church ladies arrived at 7 A.M. and set up a coffee and snack stand in the garage. It was overcast and bitterly cold. People began arriving almost as soon as it was light, snug in insulated coveralls, the only dress reasonable in the grey chill, biting winds, and occasional snow flurries. They milled around the barns and examined the stuff on the flatbed trailers, which we had pulled into the implement shed. By the time the auction started at 10 A.M., cars and trucks were parked a quarter of a mile in all four directions, marking the corner of our generational farm. *Right here. This is where it was. X marks the spot, if you see it from the air.*

You knew the auctioneer well, Brady O'Connor. It was with sympathy that he greeted Mama that morning. Mama was brave, I tell you that! She made two pies for the church ladies to sell, put on her blue parka with the fir hood, and took the pies to the garage. The church ladies greeted us, "Oh, you needn't have done that!" But they knew that she had to do what she always had done: contribute. They offered us hot chocolate. Then Mama stood with Dorothy and me to watch the auctioneer, linking arms. Occasionally she wiped a tear before it could freeze.

The coveralled buyers averted their eyes, knowing what this meant to us. And we watched as the physical proof of our family history was dispersed: Brady would call out, "Here is a woodworking set, complete, good shape, who will start the bidding? $75? Do I hear-75? 75! Do I hear 80? 85! Okay, 90!" He was fast and pushed the price. "Gone! For $95 to the man in the blue hat!" and he moved to the next item. After the smaller items were auctioned, his auctioneer's wagon was pulled around the property from implement to implement, from piles of lumber to antique doors, until everything had been auctioned. People carried off 150 years of history, as if it had never happened. Farmers and collectors pulling trailers loaded tractors and antique wagons, augers and grain drillers. By 3 P.M. it was over. Now, like ravens, scrap metal people picked clean all that was left.

As it was growing dark, we sat around our old kitchen table with Brady, and he counted the profits: $40,000. That is what it all added up to. None of us could stop it; it had to go this way. There simply was no other cure.

5

I hate to tell you this next part, Dad. It's another of those things that I am glad you never lived to see. I had a responsibility in it, for sure, but then we always do. It has taken me a while to accept the dark harvest.

I will never forget that warm, March day. I had returned from the auction worn, sad, and resigned. Jimmy and Kate would be moving into the farm house, remodeling the kitchen, and Mama to town. I would return in a month to help her. I couldn't picture it. Again, I wove. What else was there to do?

When I look back now, I can see it coming, as one can so often in hindsight. Jake had always seemed solid, like the ground I stood on, like the ground you farmed, and Grandpa farmed, and Great Grandpa farmed. Right there I should have been suspicious. Nothing is unchanging. But like our family, I couldn't suffer the change, so I denied any contrary evidence.

My increasing withdrawal contributed. Kristen's playing would call me back; her nursing filled me with pleasure. Yet I also had a growing awareness of the sweet illusion I was creating while I held her. I wouldn't do it any differently, believe me. The illusion provides its purpose; it creates a blueprint, an invaluable foundation. I would never deny Kristen the blueprint, as you did not deny me. It's just that I was learning how impermanent the houses we build are, how we can so easily outgrow them, and like the sea urchins become trapped in houses too small, perhaps the homes of our ancestors.

I did not want to see the evenings Jake spent at meetings, his tolerance of my withdrawal from him. I wanted to believe that everything was the same. So I was shocked that day Kristen and I dropped in to see Jake at the University. "We'll take Daddy to lunch," I said to Kristen as we drove to the campus that lay in a valley once populated only by fields of wildflowers and valley oaks. "Da-da, Da-da," she repeated, drooling. She was cutting teeth.

Jake's office is on the third floor of the science building. I climbed the stairwell, Kristen heavy on my hip, remembering the first time I climbed the stairwell back in the days of Dr. Witzweier. I liked remembering those days and the excitement of a world blooming. I remembered Jake's eyes, penetrating, and the first time we made love. Perhaps even this experience was the home of an ancestor, and I wanted to crawl back in, although I see now things had changed too much for that.

I knocked once and opened the office door. The room was small with a large picture window running the entire width of the facing wall. The glare backlit an embracing couple. As my eyes adjusted, I realized one of the couple was Jake. I stood there, paralyzed.

"Oh my god, Angela!" Jake disentangled himself from the young woman who must have been half his age. She straightened her miniskirt, stepped back into a shadow, stared at the floor.

I heard a roar. It was the collapse, the nucleus of the world imploding. I'm not sure how long I stood there, nor how long Jake did. I stared at him, his eyes reflecting a shared horror.

"Da-da, Da-da!"

The roar quieted; I turned to leave.

"Angela, wait. It's not what you think."

"What the hell do you mean? That you were not really kissing her? Is that what it's not?" I opened the door, felt a sob shake me. I felt Jake's hand on my shoulder.

"Honey, wait."

"Damn you, Jake. Damn you!" I started to run down the hallway. Kristen was crying. I hugged her.

"Wait, Angela, let's talk, come on, honey ..."

Reaching the stairwell, I took the steps two at a time, a waterfall tumbling toward somewhere I knew nothing about. When I pushed the exit door open, the brightness hurt my eyes and blinded me a moment. I tripped, instinctively catching myself with my free hand to protect Kristen. Jake tried to take her, but I wouldn't release her. "Leave her alone," I hissed. My wrist throbbed, both knees burned. My rage and hurt picked me up and propelled me forward. "Leave us both alone! Leave us all alone!" I ran through the parking lot to my car.

"You can't drive, you're too upset." Jake was running beside me.

"Just watch me," I seethed, opening the car door and strapping Kristen still screaming into her car seat.

"Let me drive you home."

"Get back!" I shoved him and got into the driver's seat. Jake held the door. I started the motor and backed up as he leaped out of the way. I didn't check the rearview mirror to see if he watched me go.

He said he did. Later, when we had had several weeks to cool down, after I'd thrown his clothes onto the deck and he had moved to a room nearby, he said he had considered following me, but that day he was worried it would only make me more reckless.

And he was right. I was beside myself with rage. What exactly was I raging against? Jake? Certainly Jake! He had it coming! But even then, I knew my feelings were much bigger than Jake's betrayal. I was raging against loss, against the forces that had disassembled our farm, against the blueprint's illusion that there is security.

Those weeks I could not weave. No color could approximate, no form approach, the shattered state I was in. I could not tease stray thoughts and feelings into a meaningful pattern, nor could I hold the larger whole in my heart.

6

"Angela?"

"Yes."

"This is Jake."

"I know."

"I'm sorry."

Silence.

"I'm not sure what else to say, but I'm really sorry."

Silence.

"Please say something."

"I have nothing to say."

"I know you're angry."

"No. I'm not angry. I was, but I'm not now."

"You have every right to be angry."

Silence.

"Angela?"

"What?"

"I love you."

Click.

7

"Angela, don't hang up, please."

Click.

8

"Angela?"

"Yes."

"This is Jake."

"I know."

"Can we talk? I need to talk to you, Angela."

Silence.

"Please, Angela, please..."

"You should have talked earlier."

"I suppose so. I'm sorry..."

Click.

9

"Angela, don't hang up, please listen, for the kids' sakes, don't hang up, I love you, for the kids' sakes we have to talk."

"I have nothing to say."

"When will you? Maybe if you just start you will. Please, Angela, this is killing me. Please."

"Killing you! I feel like I'm bleeding to death. I feel like someone has just yanked out my heart. I feel cut wide open. I'm hardly in shape to talk. Not yet." Click.

10

"Boys, I have to talk to you. This is really difficult. Dad is getting a place of his own for a while."

"Why?" Trent asks, stricken.

"There are some problems that have come up..."

"Like what?" Wheat sits forward, staring intently at me. The air reverberates with shock.

"It's hard to know exactly. I mean, this happens sometimes. Daddy and I loved each other very much, but a distance has come between us, so we need time apart."

"Sounds like you need time together." Trent's voice quavers.

"I can see how you'd think that, but there are some problems that have come up, too, and now we need some time away from each other."

"Where's Dad going?" Wheat asks instead of crying.

"He's getting a room in town."

"Will we see him?"

"Of course."

"Does he want to leave or are you throwing him out?"

"I'm not throwing him out, and he doesn't want to leave."

"Sounds like you're throwing him out."

"No, he just cannot live here. Not now."

"Because why?"

"Because he has a girlfriend."

Silence explodes.

"Dad has a girlfriend?"

"Yes."

"What's her name?"

"I don't know."

"How long has he had a girlfriend?"

"I don't know. A while."

"That makes me mad! He's married to you."

"I know."

"If he gets rid of the girlfriend can he come back?"

"I don't know."

11

Can you still hear me, Dad? I'm losing track of you. I can't feel you like I used to. You are fading, like a pressed rose, like an echo racing off down a canyon.

Maybe you can't hear me, but please try. Life has exploded, and this time it's not exciting. This time I'm scared. There's no refuge, no farm to return to. There's nothing to remind me of who I am. I could use that dime. "Hey, Dad, I'm in California, my life has collapsed. Can you come after me?"

12

"Angela?"

"Yes."

"This is Jake."

"I know."

"Let's talk."

"I'm listening."

"I mean let's get together and talk."

Silence.

"Angela?"

"Yes."

"I've been a fool."

"I know."

"She doesn't mean that much to me. I'm not seeing her. I want to come home."

Silence.

"There will be no others. Only you."

"How can I trust you."

"I give you my word."

Silence.

"Can I come home?"

Click.

13

A dream: A man has killed an enormous pair of rattlesnakes and hung them in a tree along the road Jake and I used to drive during our courting days. It is the same road where the fire started the week we bought our house. After the sun burned orange for two days, there was talk it could burn our woods. Fires are fertilizing, Jake had said. They make mineral soil. They clean up the forest floor. They help redwoods germinate. But faced with the thought of our own woods burning, and our home, we hoped we would not have to suffer this fertilizing energy.

The man in the dream hung the serpents horizontally in the branches, crucifying them. At least I don't have to worry about a snake returning to avenge its mate's death, I thought in the dream.

14

"Angela?"

"Jake."

"I love you. I want to come home."

"Why did you do it?"

"She was willing. It was fun. It didn't mean anything."

"What if I had done it?"

"I'd be furious."

"Why did you do it?"

"I don't know, I really don't. I've thought about it long and hard. There's a distance that's grown between us..."

"So you had an affair?"

"I shouldn't have. But our lives have gotten so separate that at the time it didn't feel wrong."

"But it was."

"It was. But I guess I was lonely."

"So you fucked a kid?"

"Not a kid, a woman. I'm sorry, honey, I really am. I want us to work on it."

Silence. Click.

15

"Angela?"

"What, Jake?"

"Don't you dare hang up. What I want to know is, do you miss me? Or are you glad I'm gone? Are you using this as an excuse to get rid of me?"

"What are you talking about?"

"You are making no effort to work this out."

"I'm angry."

"You are making no effort to work this out."

"How could you know? It's taking me a while to get used to the idea my husband has affairs."

"Damn it, Angela. You let me crawl around, begging for a word with you. Begging you to grace me with your presence."

"Well pardon me..."

"Now wait."

"Wait is right. You've hardly been waiting around on me, Jake, at least not for very long. In fact, I've been too damn tolerant of your absences."

"*My* absence! What about yours, Angela? You've been withdrawn for such a long time. You've done nothing but weave. You'd rather weave than eat. You'd rather weave than fuck."

"That's not true."

"Yes, it is."

"No, it's not." Silence. "I've got to go." Click.

16

Jimmy's third shocking call came just before the boys' Easter vacation. "Angela, Mama's been admitted to the hospital. She collapsed as we were moving her into the house. She has pneumonia. Can you come?"

Of course, I could come. I made arrangements: Kristen and Trent would go with me; Wheat chose to go with Jake to Texas. The night before we flew back, I dreamed Trent and Wheat had a small green cobra in the bathtub. They were young, perhaps six and seven, and they called to me, *Come get the snake!* I responded by stepping backwards out of the bathroom, pulling the door closed. Even as I did so, the snake reared up, suddenly expanding in size to enormous length, and slithered under the door. It was too late for Wheat to capture it. I knew I must be the one to do it. It brushed my right hand; it was cool and smooth. I awoke, knowing I would grab it.

Lying Fallow

SIX

According to ancient belief, when the snake had fulfilled its long span of life, it consumed itself and by feeding on its own body was reborn or resurrected. This led to identification of the snake with deity, infinity, immortality, and perennial renewal of life through death.

Will Barker, *Familiar Reptiles and Amphibians of America*

1

What does it mean to, finally, pick up a snake? And what does it mean to crucify two? "Those are big dreams!" Marcy said when I called her later. "Not just the *oh-my-god-let's-scream* variety!"

I tried not to feel insulted with this characterization of my attitude, telling myself that, after all, she was not Midwestern. Besides, I had to admit, she was right.

Along with these questions, I ask a third. If the creator god was a primordial boa after all, what then is implied about the nature of God? This is a heretical question, one I would have never considered asking in Sunday school. The serpent was the tempter, the devil, not, as the Gnostics held, an allegory of Christ! If we are to survive as humans, or, might I say, even *create* that which is human within us, must we crucify primordial reptilian instinct, also that root of our liveliness, by suffering painfully conflicting feelings? Must we at once hold our love and our hate for those closest to us; our longing for communion along with the great draw of the silence of self solitude? Is enduring these tensions our only hope of redemption?

2

Jimmy picked us up at the airport, Kristen, Trent, and me. I told him we'd meet him on the sidewalk outside the terminal, and there he was leaning against the passenger door. When he saw us, he came, took the bag from my hand and the carryon from my shoulder. Trent carried the other bag and Kristen buried her head in my neck, suddenly shy.

Jimmy smiled. "Hello there, young lady," Kristen burrowed further into my neck. "Hi, Angela." He gave me a quick kiss on the cheek. Then, "and look at this guy here," slapping Trent on the back. "He's grown a foot."

"Hi," Trent said, also shy.

Jimmy turned to me. "Did you have a good flight?"

"Eventless. Kristen slept most of the way, which was good, because we hit turbulence over the Rockies and they wouldn't let us up the rest of the flight."

Jimmy effortlessly lifted my bag into the back of the pickup. Trent imitated his movements, but with not the same grace. Kristen looked around again. "I have a baby seat for her," Jimmy said. "Kate insisted. She borrowed one."

"Great!" I said, opening the door. The cab was wide and seated four, but the car seat made it tight. The seat was next to Jimmy. I strapped Kristen in and sat beside her. Trent squeezed in between me and the door. He was quiet, less brave without Wheat. There was a faint smell of manure that stung my nostrils. "Do you have cattle now?" I asked as Jimmy slid into the driver's seat and slammed the door.

"John and Michael are raising steers," he said. "4-H. Got two calves from Dale Wilson. They plan on going for grand champion at the fair. One might make it, too. Those steers are from good stock."

We talked small talk as we circled out of the airport onto the freeway and across the Mississippi toward Flat Rock. Trent remarked on the size of the river. Kristen silent from strangeness watched Jimmy darkly. We did not mention Jake's and my separation, although the fact of it permeated the atmosphere. Jimmy said Mama was doing as well as could be expected considering her weakened condition when she got the flu and then pneumonia, and that the doctor said she should be able to come home the next day. He said that she liked her new house in Flat Rock, that it was more efficient.

"Kate and I are glad you could make it, Angela," he said. "Mama's been worried about you. It will do her good to see you."

I ignored the reference to me. "She hasn't been the same since Dad died." I said.

Jimmy said nothing. He just nodded.

"She was a wreck when she visited us in California," Trent blurted out. "We made her nervous."

Jimmy saw the chance to lighten the conversation. "You're kidding! Can't imagine that!"

"She can't handle much," Trent answered seriously.

"In all fairness," I said, "she had a lot to handle. The anniversary of Dad's death. The sale of the farm."

"The divorce," Trent piped in.

"We're not divorced," I corrected.

"Well, she's never quite recovered," Jimmy said. Lowering his voice he added, "She's gone downhill fast."

3

He was right. She had gone downhill, even since February and the sale. In fact, it seemed more like a plunge. "Angela," Mama said weakly as I entered 213A. As I hugged her diminished frame, I heard her weeping and did not turn her loose for some time. Jimmy was holding Kristen, and she screeched, "Momma! Momma!" stretching her arms toward me. Shaken, I lightened my grip on Mama to reach for my daughter.

Mama's cheeks were damp. "Trent, my how you've grown!" she said, grabbing his hand.

Trent was taken aback, too. "That's what Uncle Jimmy said." His voice cracked.

"Kristen, here's Grandma," I said, trying to stop the growing panic within me. Mama was pale as bone.

Mama ran the electric bed to a sitting position. "Just look at this child," she said of Kristen. Kristen clung to me koala fashion.

"Are you still slated to come home tomorrow, Mama?" Jimmy asked.

"As far as I know," she answered. Color was coming into her cheeks. "Angela, would you hand me that robe? I'm going to sit up." I handed her a pink quilted robe that looked out of place against hospital white sheets. Then I helped her as she pushed herself to her feet and shuffled to a nearby chair. Trent sat on her bed with Kristen. The nurse came in and pulled the curtain around the woman in the other bed. Jimmy pulled up a second chair and motioned for me to sit.

I did not cry. How many times have I not cried? My throat ached. I wanted to vomit. Instead, we talked of the flight, of her trip home tomorrow, of the unseasonably cold Easter weather. "It's supposed to snow," Jimmy said.

Kate arrived. Jimmy slipped his arm around her. Mama was wilting again. Jimmy and I exchanged a glance. "We should go," I said. "We need to feed the kids, and you should rest, Mama, so you'll be ready for tomorrow." I gathered Kristen from Mama's bed and hugged Mama goodbye. We all trooped into the hall. Mama looked relieved to see us go.

When we reached the parking lot, the sun was level with the rooftops. Trent decided he wanted to ride with his Aunt Kate. "Sure thing, the boys are waiting at home to see you," Kate said. She brushed Jimmy's hand. "See you at home."

Jimmy and I climbed into the pickup. Kristen fussed, and I gave her a bottle of juice. She was asleep before we were out of town. I shifted uncomfortably. "How does Kate like living in the country?" I asked. Kate grew up in Chicago.

"She's adapting," he said.

I saw her washing dishes, staring out the window over the sink to the barns. I saw the sun peep over the top of the barns, a rising star, and then burst into a fireball. I saw her rinse her hands of suds and dry them on the thin cotton flour sack my grandmother hung over the cook stove.

Oh no, I was slipping back to the past. There are no flour sacks in Illinois these days. The days of flour sacks are over. The days of dish water suds may even be over.

"Will you remodel the kitchen?" I asked warily.

"Yes," he said, "Kate wouldn't move there otherwise. We'll put in new cabinets. Gives us more space."

"Will the kitchen look different?" I tried not to sound accusing.

"From when?" Jimmy replied, catching the tone. "From the time Mom and Dad were living there? Yeah, a little. There'll be a new island, and the cabinets will extend to the ceiling. Of course, it already is different from when Grandma was there—now there's no cook stove. And it's probably a lot different from the time it was built. There's running water."

I looked at Jimmy. He sounded irritated, but he had a twinkle in his eye. "I'm sorry, I didn't mean to pick a fight." I smoothed the vinyl seat cover with my hand. "I know it has to change. If I lived there, I'd want some changes too. But I remember it as it was." I could see the kitchen so clearly, even in the smallest detail: the pill boxes Grandma kept on top of the cook stove, the dust that collected under the coleus table by the south kitchen window. That table hasn't been there since Grandma died, yet I am comforted by the memory of it, like I used to be by Dad's lap or by Mama's arm encircling me when I crawled in their bed after a nightmare. "I know it has to change, but sometimes I feel as if I can't stand it anymore, Jimmy." My voice thinned. I felt close to tears. Jimmy said nothing, but he reached over Kristen and placed a hand over mine. His hand was warm and calloused.

Tears stung my eyes, and this time I couldn't stop them from coming. They began way back, before my forty years, and washed over me with the impact of the tidal wave I used to dream hit our house out here on the prairie. They came from far beyond the cottonwood at the end of the yard, far beyond the creek where Jimmy and I fished, far beyond the elevator at Osburnville, now so broken and dilapidated. And they came with a force that flattened. I saw the destruction as I stared from the window of the truck, tears streaming down my cheeks. I saw expanses of fields still frozen, edges manicured, Osage orange hedges cut to provide more land and easier access for the monster tractors with double wheels pulling plows three times the size of your plow. We drove by the White's old farm. The house had been bulldozed and the land was plowed and dormant.

"I thought that house was in pretty good shape," I said, dabbing my eyes with a kleenex.

"You get more from farming the land than renting the house," Jimmy explained. He said it has to be this way. He said there is no alternative. "Farming is business. It's a risk and you have to stay up with the times. It's always been that way and it always will."

"But don't you miss it, Jimmy? Don't you miss the White's barns when you look out the west window? Don't you miss the smells? The oat dust in July? You don't even raise oats any more."

He looked at me with guarded eyes, Gerad's eyes. "You are being dramatic, Angela."

"Maybe," I conceded, "but something's wrong, Jimmy. I'm not sure what, but something's wrong." And an odd thought came to me. With all this plowing and cutting and bulldozing, where do the snakes live?

4

When we were within half a mile of home, I asked Jimmy to stop the truck. This was the road I used to walk when I needed to think. Jimmy braked and turned off the headlights. We got out closing the doors quietly so as not to awaken Kristen. The sky was darkening. The world was absolutely silent. Still silent. A constellation of mercury vapor lights would soon appear on the horizon. My eyes know that landscape intimately; they have studied it a million times. Grain elevators gleaming white six miles to the east. Clusters of barns and white houses placed at neat intervals, not too close to the next cluster. Willards used to live in the house across the section. I asked Jimmy who lived there now. He said a nephew used the house on weekends and Hershel White's son leased the farm.

Through successive generations, we had drawn a checkerboard matrix across this prairie, filling it with players who all eventually faded. Neighbors grew old and died, their children had more children. Many of us, like me, moved away—so many of us moved away. After the California hills and mountains, the land looked limitless. Even under the large black clouds backlit by the fading sunset, the sky and land were magnificently open.

"It's beautiful here," I said, softly. "Just beautiful. The air is so pure."

"Why did you leave, Angela?" Jimmy had never asked this before.

"I'm not sure. I guess I needed to get away."

"Maybe you should move back. I could look after you. And, it's a great place to raise kids. Remember?"

I smiled. "I remember, Jimmy." But something stirred within, and suddenly the limitless horizon felt confining; the mesh of roads, constricting. I caught my breath. I had felt this way before. Jimmy and I leaned against the truck bed watching the mountain-like clouds reach for the dark zenith of the heavens. I let my mind search the coldness of the oncoming evening, the neatness of the plowed, fallow fields for a hint.

It's spring break my freshman year of college. I'm home for the vacation. Ken Pilsner has called to take me to his fraternity's kegger over the weekend.

"Absolutely not!" you say. "A kegger is not the place for a young woman!"

I feel a rush of heat inside. Maybe because I'd been making my own decisions all year, I wasn't ready to go backwards. "What do you mean, absolutely not."

"I mean you're not going."

"I didn't ask you, Dad."

"You're not going, Angela."

"No, Dad, I'm 19. No. This time I decide."

Stunned, you looked at me. I could only stare back. A huge, dark fissure had opened in the earth between us, and we were paralyzed on either side. Then, a sudden sadness flowed into your eyes, an expression I could not bear. Nothing in either of our lives had prepared us for this. So I did the only thing I knew how to do: I turned and walked away.

I walked to this very spot and studied the rim where the sky meets the earth. How could I have forgotten? That's when I decided. The ground was shrinking; I could not stay. I'll major in marine biology and move to California, I thought.

What would have happened had I not left? Oh, this question by which my destiny has been derived! I had to leave: I know that now, as I knew it then. There wasn't room in the industrial, agricultural groundswell following the Second World War. Very few of us stayed. It was understood that we move to the cities for jobs. But what we disregarded was the impact of leaving land ensouled with the sweat of our ancestors, land we'd been born and raised on. Only now do I wonder, at what cost?

The sky deepened from silver-blue to black. Stars popped from behind the rapidly moving clouds. Jimmy's voice broke my reverie. "We need to be getting back."

When we pulled into that familiar lane it looked very much the same as when I left in my Volvo years ago. John, tall and gangly, waved as he set down his feed bucket. We parked near the gate, and Jimmy jumped out to open my door. "Come on, Angela, let's go see John's steer."

5

The next morning I awakened as if from a bad dream. I was in my old room. Woodwork outlined the door and windows. Overhead was the antique light fixture with its dusty rose flowers scrolling about the light bulb. There was a time I felt more secure here than anywhere else on earth. I closed my eyes and relaxed into the kitchen sounds below, searching. A skillet clinking, a chair scooting across the linoleum. Which morning was it, and how old was I? Am I four, and you are butchering? Are my aunts arriving to help with dinner and then the sausage this afternoon? Or am I twelve, and you're drinking the last of your morning coffee while Mama begins breakfast for us kids? I opened my eyes. Kristen stretched on the bed beside me like the baby dolls Dorothy and I used to have. My daughter asleep in my room... or John's room now. The walls were plastered with posters of someone I did not recognize playing a guitar in lewd poses.

I decided to get up. The floor was cold on my feet. I wrapped out the chill of the room with a robe, then walked to the window where Dorothy and I used to sit after everyone else went to bed. One or two inches of snow dusted the yard and fields. The sky was threateningly gray. A small family cemetery rested a quarter mile to the west, the plot where Gerad is buried.

Kristen awakened, startled, then delighted to find herself in my bed. "Mommy," she said, patting my pillow. I changed her diapers and then we went downstairs.

Bacon crackled in a cast iron skillet on the stove, and Kate stood beside it stork fashion in blue jeans and a burgundy sweater. "Morning," she said. "Sleep well?"

"Oh fine," I said. "It snowed last night. Trent is going to be delighted."

"He's already out with John and Michael doing chores," Kate said. "Have some coffee. Is there anything special you need for Kristen? Not sure she eats bacon and eggs yet."

"I've got some rice cereal for her," I said. "I might smash one of your bananas into it."

"Help yourself," Kate said. She cracked half a dozen eggs into the hot bacon fat. It sizzled wildly. There was a stomping on the back porch and excited voices. Then the door burst open and three boys entered, faces like pomegranates.

"Take those boots off over there," Kate motioned toward a register, "and get a seat, boys. Breakfast is about ready."

"Bacon!" Trent squealed. "And eggs! I'm not sure they'll sell those to Mom at home."

I turned to help Kate put the plates on the table. She was breaking six more eggs into the skillet. She gave each boy three eggs and four strips of bacon. "Pay dirt!" Trent gasped when I handed him his plate.

Jimmy stomped his feet on the porch, stomp, stomp, stomp, just like you used to, just like Grandpa used to, like Trent and Michael and John just did. I was surprised to find myself thinking that it's a good thing snow melts or there'd be a drift three miles high from men stomping their feet when they came in from doing chores in the mornings. The door burst open again. "Morning!" Jimmy said, taking off his cap. "Angela, it snowed for you."

I smiled. He wasn't so different. I always wonder what it would be like if I lived here. Would Jimmy and I be friends? Would we have long talks? Would this kitchen be less surreal to me in the wash of everydayness? This kitchen of my great-grandmother's and grandmother's and mother's, and now Kate's?

"How many eggs, Angela?" Kate was breaking more eggs into the skillet.

"One," I said.

"You eat like a bird," she laughed. "No wonder you're so skinny."

6

Jimmy ran the furnace all morning before we brought Mama home at noon. To me, her house was a stranger's house filled with familiar objects. Your chair by the couch. The piano in the entry loaded with photographs. The china dancing woman on the sideboard. Jimmy helped Mama in. She sank heavily into her overstuffed chair. "It's good to be home," she said, "though I know it doesn't look like home to you, Angela."

I smiled. "I'll get used to it, just like you have."

"Well, I'm not really used to it, but it's okay. Better in lots of ways. Smaller to clean. Closer to neighbors."

I helped her take off her coat. "Do you want to lie down before I fix you lunch?"

"Think I'll have some toast and tea first."

I fixed her toast while waiting for the water to boil. She looked better than she had the night before. She ate all the toast and sipped the tea slowly. Then she stretched out on the couch. She always napped on the couch. I got the afghan to cover her.

Her new kitchen was small, about the size of mine. I looked quickly through the drawers and cabinets, full of the pots and pans and utensils I grew up with. The refrigerator was full; Kate or Jimmy must have gotten groceries. I chopped onions in half, then chopped them into thin concentric half circles—chop, chop, chop, just as I used to watch Mama do, as I'm sure her mother did. I found the cast-iron dutch oven in the cabinet by the stove, added corn oil, browned the onions. As they sizzled, I added chunks of stew meat cut into one-inch squares and rolled in flour. I didn't know stew meat came any other size until I was eighteen and Alice Moragan's mother made a concoction with a French name, *bouef bourguignon*. It was a lot like stew, except it had much larger chunks of meat and a delicate taste I later learned was red wine.

I chopped the celery diagonally so the edges were long and the pieces thick. This is the way stew celery looks in our family. When Kristen is old enough I'll teach her to cut it this way too. I put in just one carrot because nobody likes cooked carrots much. Then I added potatoes I had peeled and cut into quarters, some water, and covered the pot, adjusting the flame. I longed to feel calm, reassured.

Then there was nothing to do. I fixed myself a cup of tea and found a spot in the living room in a rocking chair by the window. If I were home now, I'd weave, soothed by the rhythm and familiar activity. My mind would be free to roam, to search you out, or Marcy, or to swim in reverie. I thought of turning on the TV, but I dared not with Mama sleeping. I flipped through a month old *Woman's Day* and read an article on cooking sausage. The house was quiet. Occasionally a car passed on the street outside. Other than that, there was only the hum of the refrigerator and the low bubbling of the stew. I let my eyes close and remembered napping as a child, Dorothy and me upstairs and Mama on this same couch. After Dorothy was asleep I would creep downstairs and walk quietly about the living room so as not to awaken Mama. Sometimes I would watch her, her dark curly hair covering the couch pillow like weeping willow branches brushing the ground. Her eyes were closed, relaxed. I would bend closer to listen to her breath. "Angela," she might say, her eyes still closed, "get to bed this minute." Sometimes her breath was heavier and she wouldn't hear me at all. I would relax, listening to her breath, in, out, in, out...

My eyes opened. My mother lay shockingly still. I watched her chest rise and fall, catching and unsteady. Her becoming old happened too fast. When did she change from being a firm, full mother to the waning one with grayed curls frosted with more and more white? There was nothing to do but cry. A great seam unraveled and I felt myself become pieces, fraying, like being unwoven. Having a mother be so sick is being unwoven, and I sobbed some more. I could not imagine the world without her, as I once could not imagine the world without you, or Jake, and I wanted to hold on. I watched her breathe, thinking, if she stops, I'll start her, wake up, Mama! Don't die, wake up!

The back door opened. I knew it was Jimmy from his step. Mama startled awake. I wiped my eyes and cheeks with the back of my hand, feeling suddenly nude.

"Hi, Mama, Hi, Angela!" Jimmy called as he came to the living room door. I could feel him staring at me, but I ignored him as I grabbed a kleenex and blew my nose. "How are you feeling, Mama?"

"Oh, okay, Jimmy, just had a little nap. My, something smells delicious! Angela has been busy while I was sleeping. Angela..." Her voice broke off as her eyes rested on me. "Angela, you've been crying!"

"I'm okay, Mama, don't worry."

"What's wrong, honey?" Mama sat up, her attention focused on me.

"Really, I'm okay. Sometimes I just need to cry. All this change makes me sad."

"There certainly has been a lot of change, and you've always been high strung." She lay back against the pillow.

"Let me get you some stew. It must be ready. You too, Jimmy."

"I'll have some later. I've got to get over to the bank." Jimmy had sunk into your chair.

I got up and went into the kitchen. I heard the TV go on and music from a familiar soap opera. As I was ladling the stew into the bowls, Jimmy appeared.

"You all right, Angela?"

"Not really. It's going to take me a while to get used to this."

"Well, be careful around Mama." He was headed for the door.

"What do you mean?" I lay down the ladle. Jimmy's eyes widened as he turned to face me. He hadn't expected this.

"Mama's weak. She can't take much."

"What are you saying, Jimmy?" He had gone out the door and

headed down the steps. I followed, closing the kitchen door behind me. "Are you saying that if we act like something's changed here, it will kill her?" My voice was louder than I intended.

Jimmy turned to me a second, but his eyes were shielded again. "No, Angela, you know what I mean, just be careful." He walked toward his truck.

"No, I don't know what you mean, Jimmy Galway! I don't! Do you hear me, Jimmy?"

The truck door slammed and the engine started. Jimmy backed out of the driveway without looking in my direction. When I could no longer hear the truck, I noticed I was freezing and went back in, got two spoons and the bowls and went into the living room.

We watched *The Edge of Night* as we ate the stew. I used to watch it when I was home sick from high school. Nothing was familiar but the name and music.

"This is delicious," Mama said, finishing her bowl.

"Can I get you more?" I asked.

"Oh, no, Angela, no reason to overdo it. I want to be light on my feet when Kristen arrives." She chuckled, then lay back down. I tucked the afghan around her.

Kristen arrived with Kate and ran around like a mad mouse. Mama was exhausted after ten minutes of this. I took Kristen outside. The snow had melted. We walked along the sidewalk. Yellow-brown lawns merged one into the other until the town looked like one big park. I used to know who lived here. We met an old man who looked familiar, and a block later I remembered, oh yes, Will, the grade school janitor. I saw kids with faces I recognized from thirty years ago. I knew your ancestors, I wanted to say.

That evening the phone rang. Mama and Kristen had both gone to bed, and I grabbed the phone quickly so as not to awaken anyone. It was Jake.

"You all right?"

"Sure, why?"

"They think you're going off the deep end. Jimmy says you've done nothing but cry since you've been there, and he's concerned it will make your mother worse."

"Damn!" I was furious.

"I guess he called out of fear more than anything else. Concern..."

"For whom? Himself? He just wants me quiet. Whose the concern for? It's not for me. He's scared of me."

"Well, Angela, he does have a low tolerance for strong feeling, but..."

I tried to keep my voice low. "Jake, Mama is sick, she may be dying, Dad's gone, the farm is sold, you had a fucking affair, I have a healthy response, crying, and Jimmy flips out. There's only so much cooking and cleaning one can do."

There was a pause. Then Jake's voice came soft and low. "Do you want me to come, Angela? I will."

I imagined him holding me close, and like in the old days me crying into his shoulder. Ah, would I like him to come! And then again, the world shrank, as the prairie had the day before. I took a deep breath. "I'm all right. I'm just very sad, but no one can save me from that."

"Okay." Jake sounded relieved. "Oh, I almost forgot, Wheat said to tell you that he's sleeping in a room with fifteen snakes."

"He's ahead of me," I laughed.

"Maybe so. See ya."

7

We stayed the week. Mama improved considerably. Jimmy was as amiable as ever, as if nothing happened. Trent slept at the farm with Michael and John. The last day he informed me he wanted to stay.

"You can't," I answered.

"Why not?"

"School," I said.

"Let him come back in June," Jimmy said. "That kid has the makings of a real farmer. I'll give him a job mowing and he can help the boys with the cows."

I looked at Jimmy as if he were an alien. My son, work on the farm?

"Oh, please, Mom, please? "

"We'll have to talk to Dad."

"Great," said Michael. "That means yes." Then the boys left the dinner table to go out to the barns.

"They've loved having Trent here," Jimmy said. "Gives them a chance to get to know each other."

"Jimmy, Trent hasn't done farm labor..."

"So?"

"He's young."

"He's thirteen."

"He's young," I repeated. "He's my first-born."

"So?"

"Go easy," I said.

Jimmy laughed. "I'm hardly a tyrant. Just ask Mom! And if Trent gets here and doesn't want to do a thing, that's fine with me."

I smiled. Jimmy was right. He's not a tyrant, not like you could be, or our grandfathers. But then it's not a matter of survival these days either. "He's never been away for more than a week," I said.

"Do him good. Besides, Angela, you forget, I'm your brother. This is the house where you grew up. It'd do him good to spend some time on the old family farm."

I was the one who left, wasn't I? But my first-born leave *me* for several weeks? At thirteen? First you, then Jake, now Trent.

"Go easy on him, Jimmy."

Jimmy smiled. "Okay, Angela."

8

When I return home, it is already mid-April, the month the snakes come out of hibernation. It happens shortly after the last acacia blossoms dust the ground on a morning when the sky is sea-colored. Sometimes I know it has happened when I find a snake smashed like a locust pod on the asphalt during my morning walk. I feel sadness for the snake who sought warmth in the night. Sometimes I see one sunning itself on the walk by the deck.

But this first morning back from Flat Rock, I encounter a snake in the grass several inches from my chair. I'm not sure how long it's been there when I notice it. I am having my morning cup of tea. The boys caught the bus two hours ago, and Kristen, exhausted by a cold she got in Flat Rock, has fallen asleep on the deck lounge sucking her thumb and fingering her blanket.

I too am exhausted, yet clear, as one feels after a long, sad song. The emotionality has left me strangely tolerant, and I do not move. Still and clandestine, the snake is beautiful, black with yellow, the length of my arm. I watch as its tongue darts in and out. A garter snake.

For an instant, I think I hear echoes of the tractors across the prairie. The brum-m-m-m-m-m-m of Hershel White's International, the putt-putt-putt of your John Deere, sounds that soften and slow as they reach the end of each row. There is a laboring as the tractors turn, then the ecstatic, bru-m-m-m-m-m or putt-putt-putt again. In my mind's eye, I see Mama's dress flapping against her knees as she waits at the end of a bean row for you to *come get the snake*.

Above me leaves rustle. The maple across the street has light green flower-like leaves. Even those will go, I think. They will grow large and tough and dark green, and then they will be tinged yellow, and before you know it, they will be on the ground. My oldest son spending two months away this summer. My daughter already a toddler. Mama sick. I hear my grandmother's voice: "I have lived to see more than I wanted…"

Here is the snake, as he has been for ages, as he was in Illinois, as he will be in the time to come, a representative of the Great Primordial Boa! And I am beside him. Who is calling to me, *Come get the snake?* There is a bird singing. I hear each note. The snake raises his head, tongue flickering.

There are pauses in time that happen rarely, but when they do they split the world apart in their stillness and brilliance. The grass is lighted from within until it is emerald, and the yellow stripes of the snake at my feet glow. His black is the black of the earth, the decay, and wisdom.

In this state of grace, I remember the storyteller's tale of the great primordial boa who sent his child, Olodumare, to create the world. For the first time I understand that creation *begins* in grief —the god separates from his son and then the earth is created; the daughter, from the father; the dark from the light; water from the earth. This is how we gain ground to stand on, how life goes on!

A chill sweeps my body, and I yank my feet onto my chair, hugging my knees to my chest. Just as quickly, the snake slithers into the ivy.

9

In the almost-noontime sun, I go to the garden. It is so overgrown that it will take a pair of pruning sheers to cut a path from one end to the other. There are gray ashes from the wood stove coating the delicate leaves of Scotch broom at the west end of the deck, and curled orange peels and grapefruit rind halves are slowly working their way back into the earth on the ground below the middle of the deck. The sturdy green foliage of the forget-me-nots with their tiny blue flowers are everywhere. I make my way through some blackberry brambles to pick a bouquet.

As I climb the stairs back to the deck, Kristen awakens. "Momma!" I pick her up and kiss her forehead. She tastes like salt. She reaches for the forget-me-nots in my hand.

"Let's put these in a vase," I say, "and then change your diaper." She lays her head on my shoulder and I hug her tight. Even this will change, but for the first time it is okay.

Kristen watches me fix sandwiches from her high chair, and then I carry her in the chair to the deck. She's getting heavier. I won't be able to do this much longer. I give her bite-size pieces of a peanut butter sandwich. She eats one, and then hangs low over the edge, looking for the cat. Her thin, baby-fine hair stands up around her ear from sleeping on it during her nap. I smooth it with my hand. She is oblivious to this. She drops a piece of the sandwich to the deck. Nester is waiting.

"Are you done?" I lift her to the floor.

I finish eating while watching Kristen toddle about the deck. Her hair is dark, like Mama's, but in the sun it glistens auburn. Maybe the sun releases the fire inside.

Will I remember this day, this ordinary, extraordinary moment? I ask myself. Is it necessary? I have saved so many memories, so many weavings, and I see now, they become a burden. If you never let go of anything, if you never let the present slip into its ranks of past, it all builds. Better to slip it off like a snake skin, each day, each year, let the old that has become confining loosen so you can crawl out of it. You will still be there, but now you are a little larger. Isn't that the point? Not discarding your essence, only that boundary that defines your edge. The essence remains.

Kristen runs to me full speed and throws herself on my lap. "Come on, Kristen," I say. "We've been commissioned to create the world." I lift her to my hip and go to the basement to get my gloves, pruning shears, and hoe. I take the sand pail and shovel for her.

When we reach the garden, I set Kristen on the ground with her pail and shovel and loosen some dirt around her. "The storyteller said it took five days," I say, "so it's going to take a while." Kristen grabs forget-me-nots that grow like weeds along the deck and out into the plateau that Jake and I plowed years ago, before it was claimed by the snakes, presenting me with fistfuls from time to time. I pull on a young stand of Scotch broom, encouraging the earth to release the roots, to offer up the woody stems with their flaky yellow flowers. The work goes quickly. The thistles, however, take more time. They are reluctant, their roots knowing how to cling to the insides of the earth. And then there are the blackberries with their thorny shoots insistent on taking every inch of land available. I snip each shoot within inches of its root and then dig to remove the root mass.

The garden has taken its own form these years. A path here and there where Trent and Wheat have passed looking for Vera, no doubt, or going to their fort at the far corner of the orchard on the other side of the garden. A pile of rotting garbage on the west end of the deck. A rusted hoe buried in the undergrowth. I don't think of Vera. I don't think of her parents or her offspring. I don't think of the writhing snake mass. I feel my body growing damp with exertion. I salivate when I smell my daughter's head as I pick her up for a hug. I breathe deep, releasing a guttural growl as I pull a stubborn blackberry root.

Kristen digs in the spots where I have pulled out roots. I continue pulling and digging and cutting. My back aches. My hands are hot and tender within the leather gloves. A patch appears, then gradually reaches the deck and property line on the west and the fence and path to the east. I forget the time.

Kristen fusses. "Just a minute, kiddo," I say. "We are almost done." I dig another blackberry root. She drops herself at my feet and cries. I pick her up. Her diaper is soaked. I carry the hoe and pruners in my other hand. A flock of finches alight in the oak by the path. Redwoods tower toward the sky behind me. This is the end of the first day.

10

"Mom! Somebody has been destroying the weeds in the garden!" Wheat yells. He has just returned from school.

"That would be me," I answer.

"Why?! You're afraid of snakes!" His voice cracks.

"I have decided to claim it back."

"What about Vera?"

"What about her? She will still be there."

"What's gotten into you, Mom?"

I laugh and hug Wheat. "God knows!" I say.

But next morning, after the boys have left for school, Kristen and I return to the garden. This time I take a spade and shovel. "Today we dig," I say.

And we do. I push the spade deep into the earth, hearing the snaps of roots as the spade cuts through the earth. I lean my body against the spade handle and pull the dirt clod up. Pale earthworms shrink back into the dirt, insects scurry, tender and white roots grasp the dirt in my spade. I turn the dirt, chop it into smaller pieces, and press the spade into the earth again. We are the fowl scratching and spreading the dirt with shovels making a patch wide enough and dry enough for something intentional to be here too.

The dirt patch widens. It is noon. My back aches. The sun has lifted the aroma of the freshly turned earth into the air. I hear your tractor on the north forty. I walk toward you, over the deeply carved furrows. Father, I call, Father... The furrows make it difficult to walk, and I stumble two or three times. My hands meet rich dark loam.

"Mommy!" Kristen whines. She is hanging on my leg. She's hungry.

I scoop her up. She stops fussing and looks toward the house.

After lunch, she naps while I finish the garden. The worked earth spreads around me. In my mind's eye, I can see a flash of white here, a tangle of lavender there, silver greens and scarlets against a backdrop of reddish brown. My fingers crumble dirt clods. It is the end of the second day.

11

"You don't want to plant much until you know what the soil needs," Jake says the next morning when he stops by on his way to work. I can tell he's shocked I'm in the garden at all. "You should take a soil sample to the garden center."

"I thought we'd spread a few bags of cow manure," I say. That is all I remember fertilizing with in Illinois, although I know this was not the case. But it is what was memorable—the manure spreaders moving through the fields early in the spring tossing a winter's collection of strong, pungent manure across the landscape.

"The soil is different here," Jake says, always the scientist. "Better have it checked."

So I go to the garden after breakfast and collect a jar of dirt. I wonder what this dirt would like to grow besides the invasive blackberries and Scotch broom that have flourished these years of neglect.

The man at the store rubs the dirt between his fingers. "Sandy," he says. "Best thing to do is build it up with decaying matter, make humus." He sells me ten yards of partially decomposed compost which he says he'll have delivered this afternoon. He suggests I let it set a few days before planting to minimize the danger of burning the plants.

A young man a few years older than Trent delivers the rich, not yet sweet-smelling compost. We use a wheelbarrow to dump it in the garden. I rake it over the surface of the ground, then dig it in. The land is wide enough, but I've got some waiting to do. This is the end of the third day.

12

On a fog-less Saturday morning Jake and I take a cup of tea to the garden. "The ground is almost ready to plant," I say.

Jake takes a breath. "Couldn't you have gotten something odorless," he asks. "Something sterilized?" He puts an arm around my shoulder. It would be so easy to lean against him, allowing my body to mold to his. But I don't.

"This is more fertile," I say. "That's what the man said. Nothing beats a little manure."

"You can say that again."

We hear fighting upstairs. Trent has eaten three of the remaining five confection-coated donuts Wheat bought on the way home from school yesterday. "They'll handle it," Jake says. He slips his other arm around my waist as he turns toward me. I remember the first time I saw him nude on the rocks of the Humboldt coast. He was so perfect then in my mind, and so very, very exciting. But it is different now. My eyes trace the familiar line of his brow. I know what will come next, his manner of kissing my neck, his palm tracing my back, the energy in me rising to meet it.

My Beloved, my Betrayer.

Again I feel the pain. Gerad's pain? Gerad, who must also have felt betrayed by the ruthlessness of life. But then, in the end we all are betrayed, and, too, we all betray. We leave farms, wean children, grow unrecognizable to those we love. And life goes on. Life is the great primordial boa, dispassionate and harsh, but ever ready to proceed.

Jake leans to kiss me. The green specks in his eyes glisten. I hear the storyteller from last summer. *Don't wait too long. Life is very short.*

I pull back, pick up my cup of tea, warming my hands. "I don't want to slip back into what got us here," I say.

Jake does not drop his gaze. "Me either. But I love you. And we have this family. Angela. It's not just you and me, it's them too. Some things are too precious to let go." Tears well up in his eyes.

I am still angry. I want to let him suffer. But I also feel my heart burn, like it burned those days on the beach, and I know some things have to be forgiven if we are to go on. Betrayal can taint a family's lines for generations if you hold on to it.

Jake's arms enfold me. I let my body relax into the familiar sweet, sweaty smell of his chest. Upstairs are the sounds of our children. I feel at once abundantly full, and grief stricken.

Later Jake goes with me to get some plants. The boys watch Kristen. Jake helps select the fullest five-gallon buckets of rhododendrons, some plugs of blue-eyed grass, and several settings of redwood sorrel, wild ginger, and yarrow. We also get a variety of wild flower seeds: California poppy, clarkia, sticky monkey flower, baby blue eyes, blazing star. That afternoon Trent and Wheat dig holes while I work some compost into each hole. Then we place each root ball into its new home. Kristen follows Trent and Wheat. "Somebody do something about this kid," Wheat complains.

In the evening Jake and I sit on the lower deck above the garden, tired and aching. A crescent sliver of moon illuminates the evening sky, a dark plum resting in its curve.

"I could eat the moon," I say. "I could pop it in my mouth in one bite."

"It would be mushy," says Jake.

"Yes, it would squish and run down my chin and drop onto the earth."

"And up would spring violets," he continues. "Tiny violets to cover the garden." His voice is soft and low. I could float away on the waves of his voice.

"Did I tell you about April nights in Illinois?" I ask.

"I don't think so."

"You can feel it happening," I say. "The earth cut deep and receptive to the seed, the seed soon to be in exactly the right moisture and warmth to send up the sprout, it all beginning as if for the first time, again. You can smell it, it is so strong."

"What does it smell like?"

"Sex," I say.

We laugh. It is the end of the fourth day.

13

On the fifth day Jake takes Kristen and Wheat to Trent's ball game. I go to the garden and take the small loom I have been working on these past weeks. I place it in the cleared patch in the middle of the garden. Then I weave.

There is a rhythm to the loom and the yarn that eases me into another world. It is a quiet rhythm, a hypnotic rhythm, and through it a fabric is made. I am nearing completion of this piece. About the edge a snake circles and grasps its tail in its mouth. In the background are corn fields and bean fields, wheat and oat fields. I could stand in them forever.

The birds are out this morning as they are only in spring. A baby bird cheeps in the oak behind me. The osprey have returned and one flies overhead to the nest in the top of the fir. I hear the loud, characteristic, Peep! Peep!

I become sound and the sound, color. Red-winged blackbird, bluebird, bobwhite. Those are the sounds I weave now. They come from the memory of your fields, and I weave them in clear red and darting blue, subtle yet distinct browns.

Something rustles nearby. I continue weaving and listen. Vera? I wonder. A close relative? The sound is a long rustle, not the short jerky movements of a lizard. How do I weave that sound? I choose a gold yarn and fray it until I can merge it with a yarn whose green is mature and tough. Slowly I work it across the fields, listening and working, listening and working. The grassy color changes thickness and tint but continues, nevertheless.

As I weave, I remember the stories that have meant so much to my family and to me, including that of Kolowissi and the maiden. In having to leave her fatherland, she found her own ground with the beautiful sea serpent. I remember Marcy's insistence that the maiden's story was perhaps mine, too, and now I understand how this is true. For the first time since that Illinois prairie, I feel the aliveness of the

Spirit of the Earth right under my feet. Laughing to myself I picture Vera in my mind's eye, and I welcome her.

And then, in that glow of visitation of Spirit, I know that I will return to Jake. I choose him now, as I first did on the Humboldt coast. This time, though, I have the resolve to know who we each have become.

I weave until the sun drops behind the redwoods on the hill and a chill falls over the garden. When I have finished the weaving, I take the spade and in the heart of the garden, in that place where I saw the snake mass years ago, I sink the blade deep into the earth and turn it, deep into the earth and turn it, until I have a cylindrical hole. Then I sit on the earth, still warm with sun, and study the weaving. It is one of my best. Its vibrancy reaches to me. It is a skin. I can feel it loosening, and I let it. I hold it to my face, breathing its redolent scent. It smells like alfalfa and summer, and hay in winter. It smells like the grassy hills of Sonoma County, and Marcy's kitchen, and Jake's breath. Tears fertilize the fields woven there; I let them fall. I see you standing in the loam, Daddy, waving. Is it the field or my garden you stand in? It surprises me to think it doesn't matter anymore. You break a dirt clod in your hand and look into the tops of the redwoods. "It's beautiful here," you say. "Just beautiful."

I hear the car door slam and the excited voice of Wheat. "Mom! We're home." It's time to start supper, this end of the fifth day. I roll up the weaving and place it in the hole. The earth receives my seed. I trowel the dirt back in, pat it firmly, and laughing, say to no one, "From the loom to the loam!" Then I take a stick and trace a large cross over the loose earth. As if arriving in the new world for the first time, I stake my claim. *Right here. This is where I am. X marks the spot.*

I wish to express my gratitude to the group of women, *Thursday Night Writers*, who saw the potential in the snake stories long before I did. For years we have mentored each other into following the threads of the written word. Those women include: Jan Beaulyn, Norma Churchill, Elizabeth Evans, Jimalee Plank Gordon, Susan Harman, Elizabeth Herron, Dianne Romain, Leah Shelleda, and Judy Tempko. May everyone have such companions to reflect upon life's precious details and, in the process, grow one's soul.

Many thanks as well to Mel Mathews and Patty Cabanas of Fisher King Press for the enlivening publishing process any good snake story deserves.

You might also enjoy reading:

Feasts of Phantoms by Kehinde Ayeni
ISBN 978-0-9813939-2-6

Main Street Stories by Phyllis LaPlante
ISBN 978-0-9813939-1-9

Requiem by Erel Shalit
ISBN 978-1-9267150-3-2

Sulfur Creek by Thad McAfee
ISBN 978-0-9810344-8-5

Timekeeper by John Atkinson
ISBN 978-0-9776076-5-5

Timekeeper II by John Atkinson
ISBN 978-1-926715-11-7

Dark Shadows Red Bayou by John Atkinson
ISBN 978-0-9810344-7-8

Journey to the Heart by Nora Caron
ISBN 978-0-9810344-3-0

The Chronicles of a Wandering Soul by Mel Mathews
Book 1: LeRoi ISBN 978-1-926715-33-9

Phone Orders Welcomed
Credit Cards Accepted
In Canada & the U.S. call 1-800-228-9316
International call +1-831-238-7799
www.fisherkingpress.com

Made in the USA
Lexington, KY
08 May 2012